PHL
54060000003995

KT-414-546

Copper through the Ages

PLATE I

An early method of sifting and grading copper ore.
From Georgius Agricola. "De Re Metallica," 1556.

COPPER THROUGH THE AGES

Issued by the

COPPER DEVELOPMENT ASSOCIATION

Kendals Hall, Radlett, Herts.

C.D.A. Publication No. 3
First issued 1934
Ninth Revised Impression, 1953

Printed in England

FOREWORD

This book contains a brief account of some of the past and present uses of copper and its alloys. It is intentionally of a non-technical nature and will, it is hoped, be of general interest.

Technical or other information on any subject relating to the use of copper and its alloys will be supplied gladly upon request by the Copper Development Association.

The above monogram is that of the Copper Development Association. It is built up from the initial letters of the Association's title and the symbol ♀, used since ancient times to denote the metal copper.

♀ is a modified form of the Egyptian hieroglyphic symbol for enduring life. It was known as the "ankh", and appears very frequently in Egyptian inscriptions, such as the cartouche of Tut-ankh-Amen.

It is also the sign of the Zodiac for the planet Venus. The Roman goddess of that name was identified with the Greek goddess Aphrodite, one of whose principal places of worship was the island of Cyprus. The same locality was also closely associated with copper, since it was the source from which a large part of the supplies was obtained in Greek and Roman times.

G.W.P.

1934

CONTENTS

Early Brass Cannon, 14th Century.

LIST OF ILLUSTRATIONS

Casting Copper at Karnak, 1450 B.C.

Copper through the Ages

CHAPTER I

The Metal Age

Copper was one of the first metals to be employed by man and it has since played an important part in almost every phase of his activities.

The wealth and power of many of the great Empires of the past can be attributed very largely to the possession of copper, while we to-day are no less dependent upon it, for copper plays a vital part in all branches of our engineering, science and architecture, and there can be little doubt that without it the wonders of this electrical age, if not altogether impossible, would have been denied to us at least for many years to come.

The very early history of man is still the subject of so much doubt that it is not possible to record chronologically with any degree of accuracy many of the more important events which are known to have taken place. One such event was the first use of metals, and, although there is ample evidence to show that copper was certainly one of the first to be discovered, and probably the first to be employed for useful purposes as distinct from ornamentation, it is possible to estimate only vaguely the date of the occurrence. Man is generally supposed to have existed on earth for about 500,000 years, but as far as can be ascertained it seems probable that he has not been acquainted with the arts of metal working for much more than about one per cent. of that time.

It is customary to designate the two great stages in the history of man as the Stone Age and the Metal Age. The first main phase of the latter is often described as the Bronze Age; but according to many authorities it should be divided into two parts, the Copper Age and the Bronze Age proper, the Copper Age being characterised by the use of copper alone or copper with which small amounts of tin or other metals were unintentionally alloyed, a period which differed from that of the Bronze Age proper when the technique of alloying was appreciated and bronze was produced intentionally when required. In reality, however, these stages were not ages in the history of the world as a whole but rather stages in the development of its various peoples, and in different countries they overlapped.

The Dawn of the Copper Age.

The change from stone to metal appears to have taken place very gradually, there having been in most places a transitionary period, sometimes known as the "Chalcolithic" period, or the "copper-stone" age, "chalco" being derived from a Greek word meaning "copper". During this period man used metal, such as native copper, much in the same way as he had used stone, bone and shell. It is possible that he looked upon copper as a sort of malleable stone.

Although there is some doubt on the point, it is probable that there were three main stages in the development of the art of metal working. In the first instance copper found in its native state was hammered into shape, in the second it was melted and cast, and in the third, smelted from its ores. In some areas copper may have been in use for as long as 2,000 years before it was discovered that it could be obtained by smelting. That event, however, ranks in importance with the discovery of the first means for producing fire artificially and undoubtedly marks one of the great turning points in the history of man.

A "native" metal, to which reference has already been made, is one which is found in its normal metallic state and not in chemical combination with other elements. Copper and gold, owing to their exceptional resistance to corrosion, are often found in their native state, and there can be little doubt that they were the first metals to be used. Gold, however, is a very soft metal and quite unsuitable for the making of weapons or implements, for which purpose it was of considerably less value than copper; a fact which primitive man was not slow to appreciate. Attracted by the bright and pleasing appearance of copper, he found that its ductility enabled him to beat it to almost any shape that he required, and that in the process it became sufficiently hardened to enable him to sharpen it into weapons and implements of lasting quality.

If, as seems probable, copper in its native state was one of the first metals to be used, it might reasonably be assumed that the dawn of the first copper age took place in a locality where supplies were most plentiful. It is not possible, however, on these grounds, to credit any particular locality with the first use of copper. Vast quantities of native metal have been found in North America, particularly in the region of Lake Superior, but it seems very unlikely that these deposits were the first to be utilised by man, for although there is ample evidence that the inhabitants of that country in the Pre-Columbian era made extensive use of beaten native copper for ornaments and implements, there is no evidence that they employed the finer arts of metallurgy prior to the coming of the white man. It is, in fact, remarkable that they appear never to have discovered that copper could be melted, for they were still in this state of ignorance upon the arrival of settlers from the Old World, where at the time a high degree of perfection in the art of metal working had already been established for some thousands of years.

The fact that but little native copper has been found in Europe and Asia for many years past does not altogether preclude the possibility that such deposits may have existed at one time. The supply, being insufficient to meet the demand, may have become exhausted. Traces of copper workings, some dating back possibly as far as 5000 B.C., have been found at a number of places spread over a wide area now occupied mainly by the countries of Persia, Mesopotamia, Arabia, Turkey, Palestine and Egypt, including the Island of Cyprus, but the evidence tends to indicate that the art of metallurgy probably originated in that area which centres round the valleys of the rivers Tigris and Euphrates, which is believed to have been the site of the earliest civilisation.

The Early History of Copper.

There appears to have been a widespread Neolithic civilisation at the time of the first appearance of copper, which was certainly known long before the coming of the Sumerians to Babylonia, or the establishment of the First Egyptian Dynasty, for although some of the oldest copper objects found undoubtedly belong to a very early period of culture, there is evidence that the arts of agriculture, spinning and weaving were at the time well established, and that some animals had long been domesticated.

Copper objects have been discovered in Mesopotamia below the level of the clay deposit left behind by the Great Flood, which is believed to have occurred about 4000 B.C. One such object is a copper spearhead found below "flood level" at Ur in Southern Mesopotamia which, with similar evidence from some of the other earliest river sites, indicates that copper was in use in that area before 4000 B.C. Very old copper objects, thought to date from 4500 B.C. or even earlier, have also been found in graves of the Badarian type in the Fayum in Egypt. These people of Pre-Dynastic Egypt (prior to about 3200 B.C.) also used copper carbonate as a pigment. They employed copper for carpentry, the metal being worked into axes, adzes and boring tools.

It is possible that the art of metal working may have originated in Elam, a land east of Babylonia now forming a part of Iran, and that copper was introduced into Babylonia by the Sumerians at a time when a prosperous civilisation already existed there. No copper deposits existed in Babylonia, and the origin of the Sumerian supplies has been the subject of much speculation, since most early copper and bronze objects, whether found in Mesopotamia or Northern India, contain a small proportion of nickel, in spite of the fact that nearly all of the copper ores found in Asia and the Eastern Mediterranean are free from this metal. Recent investigations, however, have disclosed the fact that nickel-bearing copper ores are to be found in the State of Oman in South-East Arabia, and it is now thought possible that these may have been the source of Sumerian supplies.[1]

The First Experiments in Metallurgy.

There is some diversity of opinion as to the probable date at which it was discovered that copper could be obtained from ores by smelting. Some opinion favours the suggestion that the earliest copper objects were not made from "native" metal but from copper smelted from the ore malachite, the art of smelting being of Elamitic origin. It is generally believed, however, that the process of copper smelting had not begun to be known before about 3500 B.C., although it is probable that in some parts the metal had been melted and cast for some time before that date.

Several rather romantic hypotheses have been put forward to account for the discovery, but it seems probable that it originated in the ordinary camp fire, which thus proved to be the first metallurgical furnace, and the forerunner of its gigantic counterpart of the present day. As the late Professor Gowland suggested, it is not unlikely that the ring of stones which formed the domestic hearth contained pieces of copper ore, carbonate, oxide or mixtures, and that some of these were converted to metal by the reducing action of the fire.[2] As soon as the similarity between the beads of metal found in the ashes and the native metal, which was already well known, had been recognised, it would not have been long before the first experiments in smelting were begun.

Evidence shows that the hearth of the earliest metallurgical furnaces had a shallow circular cavity about 10 or 12 inches in diameter, in which the molten metal was collected. A charcoal or wood fire was made in the hearth and alternate layers of charcoal and ore were added. When the metal produced from the ore had run into the cavity at the bottom of the hearth, the fire was raked off, and the metal allowed to cool. At the moment of solidification the metal lump was dragged out and broken on a stone. The small pieces thus obtained were remelted for casting as required.

[1] Brit. Assoc. for Advance. of Science. Report of 96th Meeting, 1928, p. 438.
[2] GOWLAND. "Copper and Its Alloys in Early Times." *J. Inst. Met.*, vol. 7. (1912,) pp. 25-26.

In order that cleaner metal might be obtained, the cavity in the hearth was often lined with clay, and this practice probably led to the adoption of crucibles made from clay and finely cut straw or grass, which were sunk into the bottom of the hearth to receive the molten metal. These crucibles could be lifted out and the metal poured directly into the moulds, thus avoiding the necessity for breaking it up and remelting it. Furnaces of this type were in use in Derbyshire up to the seventeenth century, and in Japan as late as 1858.

The earliest furnaces relied solely on chance fanning by the wind, but in later types an attempt was made to control the air supply. Egyptian wall paintings show blow pipes in use with small furnaces as early as the Vth Dynasty (2690-2420 B.C.) and later, about 1500 B.C., they depict the use of bellows. From then onwards, there is evidence that a large variety of bellows and fans was employed, or that alternatively, furnaces were constructed on the windward side of hills, with a trench to act as an air scoop. Numerous examples of the latter type were constructed by the Romans in Cumberland.

The Introduction of Bronze.

Having no knowledge at first to enable them to distinguish between the different types of ores, a more or less pure metal was rarely obtained, and as it happened that in many parts tin and copper ores were found in close proximity, bronze, an alloy of these two metals, was sometimes produced accidentally. In the course of time, however, the advantages to be obtained by the proper alloying of metals seem to have become appreciated, for some sort of scientific control was eventually established, the constituents of the alloys being varied to suit the purpose for which they were required.

The composition of the alloys first used in any particular area depended largely upon the type of ores found in the locality, but, as greater knowledge was acquired, supplies of more desirable kinds were sought over an ever increasing area. Nevertheless the making of bronze was at all times governed by the availability of tin supplies, thus some areas seem either to have had no Bronze Age at all or a late and slowly developing one, while in other areas, copper and bronze seem to have been used

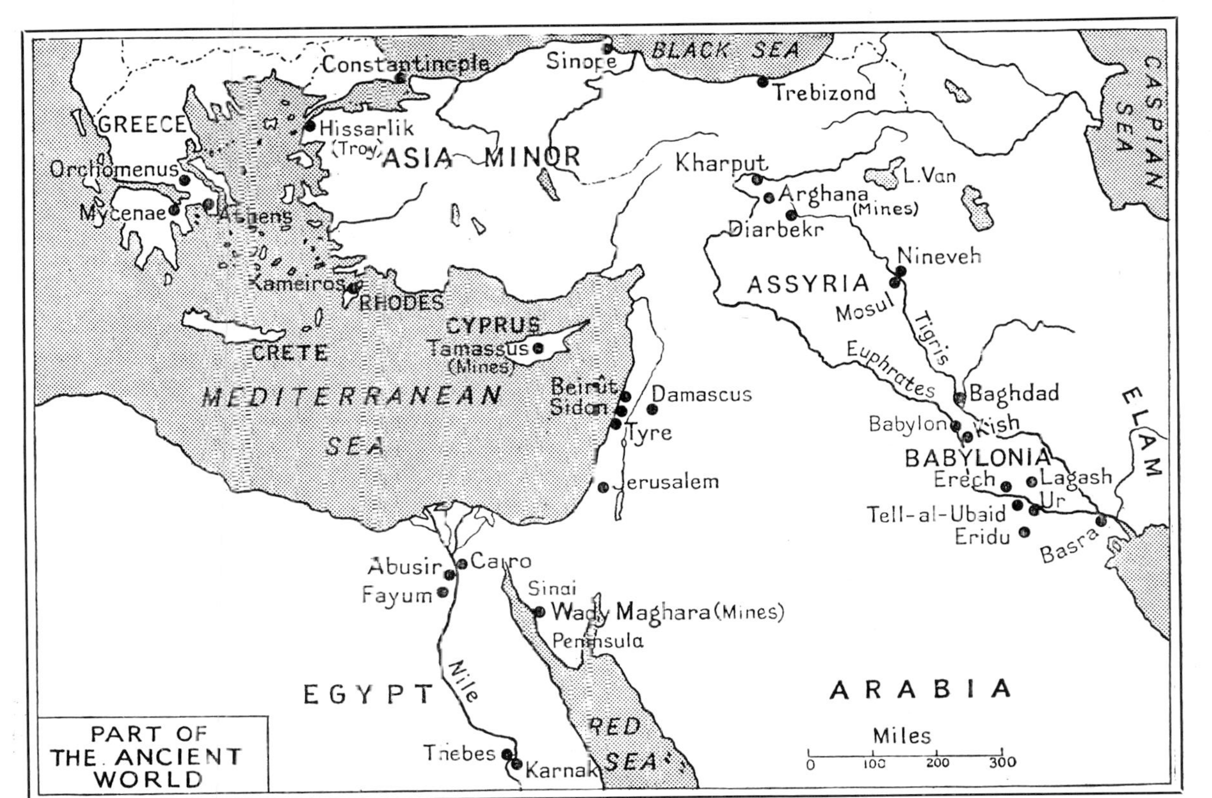
CASPIAN SEA
BLACK SEA
Constantinople
Sinope
Trebizond
GREECE
Hissarlik
(Troy)
ASIA MINOR
Kharput
L. Van
Orchomenus
Arghana
(Mines)
Mycenae
Athens
Diarbekr
Nineveh
Kameiros
RHODES
ASSYRIA
Mosul
CYPRUS
Tamassus
(Mines)
Tigris
CRETE
Euphrates
MEDITERRANEAN
SEA
Beirut
Sidon
Damascus
Tyre
Baghdad
Babylon
Kish
ELAM
BABYLONIA
Jerusalem
Erech
Lagash
Ur
Tell-al-Ubaid
Eridu
Basra
Abusir
Cairo
Fayum
Sinai
Wady Maghara (Mines)
Peninsula
Nile
EGYPT
ARABIA
RED SEA
Miles
0
100
200
300
Thebes
Karnak
PART OF
THE ANCIENT
WORLD

PLATE II

PLATE III *[By permission of the British Museum*

Ribbed copper tray and copper vessels from the Royal Graves at Ur; c. 3200 B.C. (See page 13.)

PLATE IV *[By permission of the British Museum*

Fluted copper bowl and bucket from Ur; c. 3200 B.C. (See page 13.)

intermittently. The Sumerians, for instance, after using bronze extensively, appear to have reverted to the use of copper from about 3200 B.C. to 2700 B.C., possibly owing to a failure of tin supplies. A ribbed copper tray, pan and other copper vessels found during excavations in the Royal Cemetery at Ur are illustrated in Plates III and IV. Sir Leonard Woolley, who carried out the excavations, estimated that these vessels are from a period earlier than the First Dynasty, and that they date from about 3200 B.C., although others believe that they may not be much earlier than about 2700 B.C.

The Egyptians obtained much of their copper from the Sinai Peninsula, where no tin ore is found; thus the development of a bronze age in Egypt was comparatively slow, and it is thought that the alloy was not known to any great extent in that country until about the 18th Dynasty (1580—1350 B.C.) by which time the domination of Syria by the Pharaohs had made foreign sources of tin available. The use of bronze in Egypt probably did not reach its zenith until about the time of the reign of Psamtik (663—609 B.C.).[1]

In Ireland there appears to have been a very distinct copper age lasting for about 700 years before bronze was introduced, presumably from this country, where it seems to have been used from the earliest days of metal working. The lateness of the Bronze Age in some other parts of the world is illustrated by the fact that the Peruvians were only just beginning to make bronze when they were subjugated by the Spaniards in the 16th century, while in North America there does not appear to have been a Bronze Age at all.

In many areas it is probable that tin was not known as a separate metal until the Iron Age was well advanced, and the tin ore which was used for making bronze was often replaced by that of a more plentiful metal when ample supplies were not readily available. Thus early implements found in Hungary contain antimony instead of tin, due probably to the local presence of antimonial copper deposits and a shortage of tin. Chinese bronzes also sometimes contained antimony, some Han

[1]RICKARD "Man and Metals," (1932), vol. 1, pp. 129-130.

period objects from tombs in Korea having been found to contain as much as 8 or 9 per cent. [2]

Lead was a common constituent of bronzes in many parts, and appears to have been added, sometimes to improve the moulding properties of the alloy, for purposes such as the casting of statues, and sometimes owing to a shortage of tin. Many of the Greek statuary bronzes contain large quantities of lead, which was also a very common constituent of most early Chinese bronzes, particularly during the Han Dynasty (206 B.C.—220 A.D.), though some doubt exists in the latter case as to whether this was due to a shortage of tin or an inability to distinguish between tin and lead ores. In this connection it may be noted that the Chinese character "hsi", which has been translated as "tin", was anciently used also for lead.

[2] COLLINS. "Corrosion of Early Chinese Bronzes." *J. Inst. Met.*, vol. 45, (1931), p. 23.

ANCIENT ROMAN WATER WHEEL,
ABOUT 50 B.C.

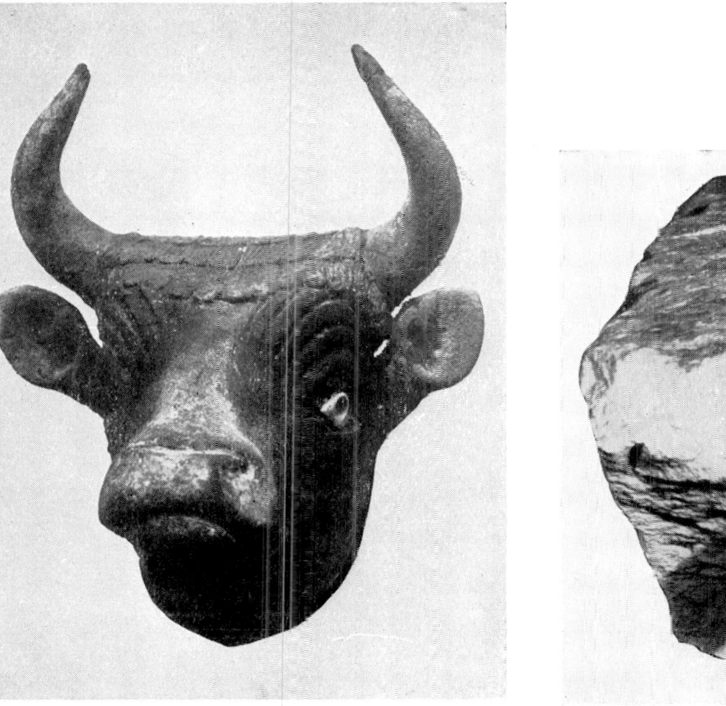

PLATE V [*By permission of the British Museum*

Cast copper bull's head found at Ur; c. 2700 B.C. (See page 15.)

PLATE VI

Section of Egyptian copper water pipe found at Abusir; c. 2750 B.C. (See page 19.)

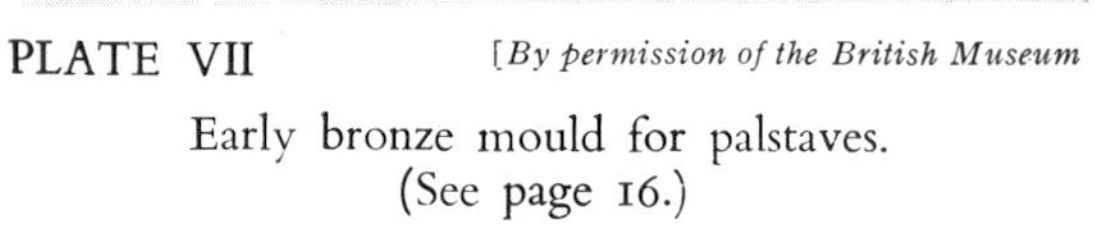

PLATE VII [*By permission of the British Museum*

Early bronze mould for palstaves.
(See page 16.)

PLATE VIII

Copper statue of Pepi II; c. 2600 B C.
(See page 16.)

CHAPTER II

Early Processes

The Development of Castings.

It is probable that the first casting was done in open sand moulds, and that these were later superseded by rock. Early examples of copper adzes and celts show that they were cast in open moulds, and the practice seems to have been to cast them of uniform thickness and then hammer them into their final shape. Hollow stone moulds were next introduced, and later in the Bronze Age both clay and bronze moulds were used, perfect castings of thin blades being obtained by heating the clay moulds to a dull red heat before pouring the metal.[1]

Excavations at Ur tend to show that the Sumerians were only just beginning to cast copper about 3100 B.C., since the very variable skill displayed in the casting of some of the objects of that period which have been found indicates that the art was in an undeveloped state at the time. The cast copper bull's head belonging to a "plaster" lyre dating from about 2700 B.C. or earlier, which is illustrated in Plate V, was found during excavations in the Royal Cemetery at Ur, and is a particularly fine example of early ornamental copper casting.

There is evidence that the Egyptians and Greeks acquired great skill in casting. Most of the ancient Greek statues were solid, but those of Egyptian origin were light and hollow, having been cast with a sand core, which still remained in many of the examples which have been found. It is also believed by many that the Egyptians invented the "cire perdue" or waste wax process of casting, a description of which is given later.

Among the earliest objects yet found which may possibly have been partly cast by this process are statues of Pepi I and his son dating from about 2600 B.C. There is some doubt, however, whether the process was actually used by the Egyptians

[1] Gowland. "Copper and Its Alloys in Early Times," *J. Inst. Met.*, vol. 7. (1912), p. 34.

at this date, although Garland has stated that a copper spout from a water vessel which he examined and which was authoritatively attributed to a period even earlier than this, was undoubtedly made by the wax process.[1] The above-mentioned statues are now in the Cairo Museum and it is noteworthy that an analysis of the metal of which they are made shows that it consists of 98·2 per cent. of copper, 1·06 per cent. of nickel and ·74 per cent. of iron, the point of interest being the very high percentage of nickel.[2] A photograph of the statue of Pepi's son, Pepi II, is reproduced in Plate VIII.

In Plate VII is illustrated a type of split bronze mould used in this country for the manufacture of palstaves. The mould itself appears to have been cast in clay; for its construction a model palstave was used.

Many ancient Chinese bronze objects are also thought to have been cast by the cire perdue process, some perhaps as early as 2255—2205 B.C., and a few interesting examples are shown in Plates IX—XII. Of the objects illustrated, the bell shown in Plate XI is probably the oldest and is thought to date to the Shang Yin period (?1766—?1122 B.C.) or the early part of the Chou period which followed. The object illustrated in Plate X is of particular interest, for although it dates perhaps from the early part of the Chou period (?1122—249 B.C.) it bears a remarkable resemblance to a present-day tea-pot. It was known as a "Ho" or "Huo" and was used probably as a container for water or wine.

Chinese Metallurgy.

Little is known, however, of very early Chinese metallurgy, although examples of bronze work have been found which may date back to the ancient Shang-Yin (?1166—?1122 B.C.), or even the legendary Hsia dynasties. Examination of these objects unfortunately provides no certain clue to the practices prevailing at the time when the original alloy was made, since there is always the possibility that the metal may have been recast from objects of some still earlier period. Practically the only written record of early metallurgical practice is that given

[1] GARLAND. "Ancient Egyptian Metallurgy" (1927), p. 35.
[2] Brit. Assoc. for Advance of Science. Report of 96th Meeting, (1928), p. 439

PLATE IX [*By courtesy of George Eumorfopoulos, Esq.*

Ancient Chinese sacred vessel. Cast bronze—Chou period.
(1122—249 B.C.) (See page 16.)

PLATE X

PLATE X

Ancient Chinese vessel, probably used as a container for water or wine. Cast bronze—Early Chou period (?). (See page 16.)

PLATE XI

Chinese bell. Cast bronze—Shang Yin or Early Chou Period; c. 1200 B.C. (See page 16.)

PLATE XI

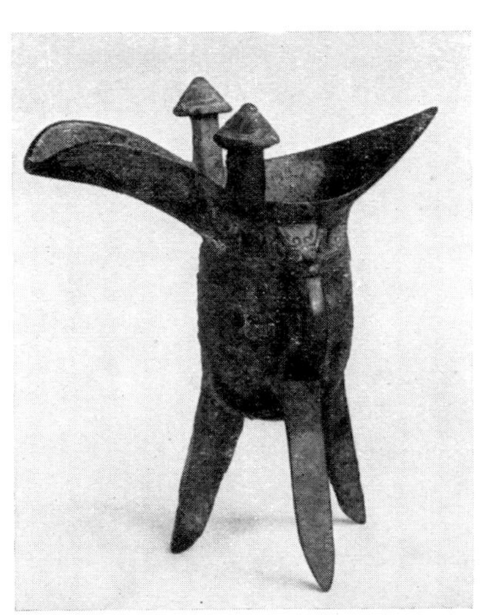

PLATE XII

PLATE XII

Ancient Chinese wine goblet. Cast bronze—Chou Period (?). (See page 16.)

[*By courtesy of George Eumorfopoulos, Esq.*]

in the section of the ancient book, "Chou li", which is entitled "K'ao kung chi", and is of uncertain date. This account appears to be of a rather theoretical nature, and there is doubt as to whether it is a true record of the actual state of the art.[1]

Copper was looked upon in China as the metal "par excellence", and for that reason was referred to as "chin" (metal) in the above-mentioned document. Objects cast in bronze were divided under six headings, and the most suitable proportions of copper to tin were given as follows:—

(1) Cauldrons and bells	5—1
(2) Axes	4—1
(3) Halberts and spears	3—1
(4) Swords and knives	2—1
(5) Erasing knives and arrows	3—2
(6) Mirrors and specula	Equal parts

In view, however, of the very high proportion of tin and the fact that lead is not mentioned, the accuracy of some of these formulæ would appear to be questionable. The formula for mirror bronze, for instance, is particularly doubtful, since mirrors made by other nations usually contained about two parts of copper to one of tin, that composition being found to give the maximum power of reflection.

It is probable that the casting of mirrors in China began about the latter part of the Chou period, for it is certain that they were in existence before 206 B.C. They were often elaborately decorated, but unlike the Roman mirrors, such as that illustrated in Plate XIII, they had no handles, being fitted instead on the back with one or two loops to which a cord could be attached. Very large numbers of these mirrors appear to have been manufactured in early times, possibly on account of the magical properties which they were supposed to possess.

At a later date it was not unusual for bronze mirrors made in Japan also to have magical properties, although in this instance the properties were such that they could be easily demonstrated. The mirrors, which were cast in a mould, usually had ornamentation in relief on their backs, and although the surface of a mirror

[1] YETTS. Catalogue of the Eumorfopoulos Collection, vol. 1, p. 34.

after polishing appeared to be quite uniform and gave an apparently undistorted image, when light was reflected from it on to a wall or other flat surface there appeared in the reflection a reproduction of the pattern on the back of the mirror. This phenomenon was for a long time a mystery even to the Japanese themselves, until the reason for it was eventually discovered by Professor Ayrton.

After a mirror had been removed from the mould it was laid on its back to be polished. This was done by first scraping the surface very heavily with a blunt tool and then finishing it by applying charcoal and scrubbing with paper, after which the mirror was "silvered" by the application of an amalgam of tin and mercury. The violent scraping of the mirror caused it to bend and become slightly convex, the thin parts yielding more under the pressure than the parts where the pattern on the back made the mirror thicker, and so the thick parts became worn away rather more than the thin ones. A slightly concave reproduction of the pattern on the back was thus formed on the surface of the mirror which was, however, too slight to be noticeable except when light was reflected from the surface.[1]

The Cire Perdue Method of Casting.

The cire perdue process of casting was used extensively in China, but the only record of it is a very incomplete one given in a 13th Century work. Two methods were in general use. In the first a core model was built up to conform roughly with the lines of the finished object. This was coated with several layers of wax, upon which the exact details of the object were cut. The whole was then encased in an outer mould of clay or other suitable material which was then hardened, the wax melted out, and the metal poured in.

A second method, whereby numerous copies of an object could be made, consisted of applying clay or plaster to the object and then removing it in sections. These were thinly coated with wax and carefully re-assembled. Hot wax was poured in, and the mould rotated until the required thickness of solidified wax was obtained on the inner walls. Upon removal of the mould a complete wax model remained, which could be embedded

[1] SILVANUS THOMPSON. "Light Visible and Invisible" (1897), p. 50.

in a suitable moulding material for treatment as in the first method. The necessary air vents and runners for the metal were fashioned in wax, and additional ornamentation was frequently applied to the wax model by means of dies.

There is a traditional belief in China that metal came from the West, and it is well known that two trade routes existed from that country via the Altai and Lake Balkhash regions of Siberia, and the Tarim and Turkestan respectively. Although ancient Chinese metallurgy, with its free use of lead, differs from that of the Sumerians, whose bronze seldom contained more than about 1 per cent., it is not improbable that a knowledge of the art did spread to China from the West.

The Use of Copper by the Near East and Mediterranean Civilisations in Early Times.

The Egyptians used copper extensively in architecture as well as for ornaments and household utensils. Temple doors were often made of copper and even water pipes were sometimes made of that metal. A section of pipe made from beaten copper sheet which was laid in a rock trench and covered with gypsum in the temple of King Sa-hu-Re at Abusir about 2750 B.C. is now in the Berlin Museum and is illustrated in Plate VI.

Numerous finds at Al 'Ubaid, near Ur, dating from about 3100 B.C., show that copper sheets were wrought and hammered over carved wooden work, usually being fastened with copper nails or by copper wires set in bitumen. To these belongs the magnificent Imdugud Relief, which represents a lion-headed eagle holding two stags by their tails. The whole relief is of copper, within a copper frame, on a wooden background; the overall dimensions being 7 ft. 9½ in. long and 3 ft. 6 in. high. The stags' antlers, which are in high relief, were made of wrought copper and soldered into their sockets with lead. (See Plate XXX).

That copper and bronze were used also in other parts is evidenced by objects such as those which have been found in the lowest stratum of the First Prehistoric City of Hissarlik, which stood on the site of ancient Troy near the entrance to the Dardanelles. Specimens of metal work found there show that about 3000—2500 B.C. copper or bronze had already been in use for many years, since the finds include knives having rivet holes which indicate a degree of metallurgical knowledge and technical skill that could only have been attained long after metal was first known.[1] Copper objects, including two large nails of fairly pure copper, one weighing 2½ lbs., have also been found in the ruins of the second city of Troy, while copper nails which belong to the remote Mycenæan period of Mediterranean civilisation have been discovered elsewhere at Orchomenus, a city in Bœotia, which was in decay at the time of Homer.[2] Similar evidence shows also that copper and bronze were employed for cramps in buildings and for many other purposes as well as for weapons and implements.

At a later date, Hesiod mentions a building which had a copper roof.

Large quantities of bronze were used for utensils and vessels in Nineveh in Northern Mesopotamia about 1000 B.C., and a collection of such objects found by Layard is now in the British Museum. Copper and bronze were also used extensively in the Greek Peloponnesian War; but although these metals were also used at the time for statuary and many other purposes, it was not until the fall of Greece and the rise of the Roman Empire that one of the most important periods in the history of copper really began.

The Romans made considerable use of copper and bronze not only for statues and objects of art but for vessels, furniture, domestic articles and a variety of architectural and other purposes. Bronze was used even for such purposes as surgical instruments and artificial limbs; a delicately fashioned artificial leg, dating from about 300 A.D., made from bronze sheet which was originally fixed to a wooden core by bronze nails, is still preserved in the museum of the Royal College of Surgeons. The Romans, like many others, also made razors of bronze, and from an examination of some of the types which were used, such as those illustrated in Plate XIV, it is perhaps surprising that beards were not more popular than they appear to have been.

Some of the earliest Roman bronze which was used for coinage about the 5th century B.C. contained large proportions of lead

[1] GOWLAND. "The Metals in Antiquity." *J. Roy. Anthropological Inst.*, vol. 42, (1912), p. 247.

[2] GOWLAND. "Copper and Its Alloys in Early Times." *J. Inst. Met.*, vol. 7, (1912), pp. 35-36.

and except for a period of about 200 years from 20 B.C. onwards, lead appears to have been a fairly regular constituent. The Romans used a copper coinage exclusively until 269 B.C., when they began to coin silver; the Greek currencies were always silver, their copper coins being negligible. The Roman *As* probably signified originally one pound weight of uncoined copper. It was divided into twelve ounces, the first six of which were represented by copper coins. The earliest Roman copper coins were not struck, but were cast in stone moulds. Frequently the impression—a two-headed Janus on one side and the prow of a ship on the other—was struck afterwards on the plain discs, upon an anvil.

The inclusion of lead in Roman statuary bronze was probably due to Greek influence, but unless it was for the sake of cheapness there does not appear to be any reason why it should have been included in bronzes for engineering purposes, for which it rendered the alloy less suitable. A broken water wheel shaft found in the lower Roman workings of the north lode of the Rio Tinto mine in Spain contained about 77 per cent. copper, 10 per cent. lead and 9 per cent. tin, and is thought to date from the time of Vespasian in the first century of our era.

The Introduction of Brass.

Brass, an alloy of copper and zinc, appears for the first time, probably accidentally, in a ring from the Cemeteries of Armant,[1] which contained 31·1% of zinc and is probably older than 2000 B.C. The Greeks were acquainted with brass, for an Aristotelean writer refers to "oreichalkos" a "brilliant and white" copper made by the Mossynocci by mixing tin and copper with a peculiar earth known as "calmia" from the shore of the Euxine.[2] Undoubtedly, "calmia" was a zinc ore, a carbonate or silicate similar to that later known as "calamine", which was used for the manufacture of calamine brass. The alloy was made by heating a mixture of ground calamine ore and copper in a crucible. The heat applied was sufficient to reduce the zinc in the ore to the metallic state, but was not sufficient to melt the copper. The vapour from the zinc, however, permeated

[1] Mond and Myres. "Cemeteries of Armant," 1937, p. 119.

[2] The Mossynoeci were a people who lived on the southern shore of the Euxine or Black Sea, between the cities of Sinope and Trebizond.

the copper and formed brass, which was then melted.[1]

Brass was known in Egypt during the first century B.C.

The first Roman coins of brass, containing about 17 per cent. of zinc, seem to have been made about the time of Augustus (20 B.C.—14 A.D.) and it is thought by some that this was the first occasion upon which brass was made intentionally. Until the time of Diocletian (286—305 A.D.) brass coins had a higher value than those of bronze, 6 parts of brass being equal to 8 parts of bronze.

The Romans used brass not only for coinage, but also for fibulæ, personal ornaments and decorative metal work. The alloy usually contained about 11 to 28 per cent. zinc, and they appear to have had a good knowledge of its most suitable composition for the various purposes for which it was required. The metal used for delicate decorative work, for instance, was required to be very ductile and of good colour; it is interesting to note, therefore that analysis has shown that the alloy used for this purpose contained about 80 per cent. copper and 18·7 per cent. zinc, and closely resembled Tournay's alloy, used in recent French imitation jewellery, and also the "gilding metal" of to-day.

In historical records the word "brass", like "bronze", appears to have been applied in a very loose manner to almost any type of copper alloy. "Brass" is frequently mentioned in the English version of the Bible, although it is probable that the metal referred to was in reality copper or bronze. The word "copper" or one of its several variants was used in England as early as 1050 A.D., but it was displaced by "brass" when Wycliffe translated the Bible in 1382, that word being retained in the subsequent translations.[2] The expression "not worth a brass farthing" actually refers to the copper farthings issued in 1613. "Brass" as we know it to-day was never used for British coinage until the recent introduction of the twelve-sided threepenny pieces, which are a brass containing 79 per cent. copper, 20 per cent. zinc and 1 per cent. nickel. Bronze coins were not minted in England until 1860. In Elizabethan times "brass" was known as "latten" a word very similar to the present-day French word "laiton".

[1] GOWLAND. "Copper and Its Alloys in Early Times." *J. Inst. Met.*, vol. 7 1912, p. 43.

[2] RICKARD. "Man and Metals" (1932), p. 162.

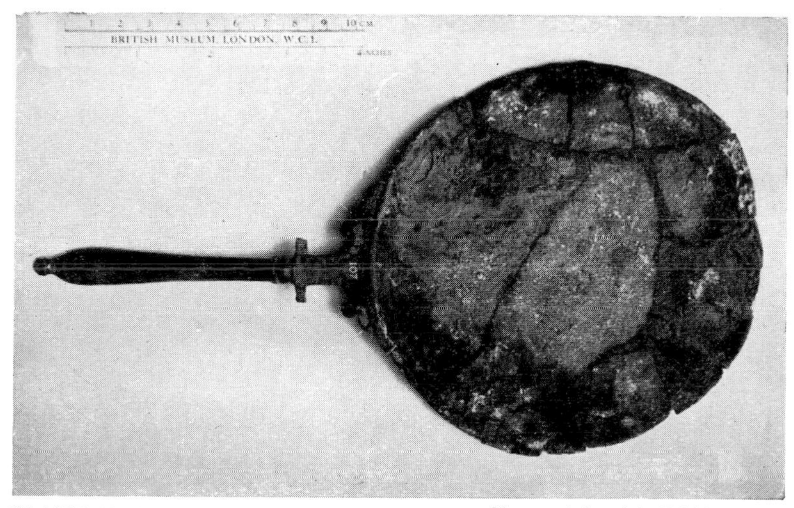

PLATE XIII [*By permission of the British Museum*

Roman bronze mirror. (See page 17.)

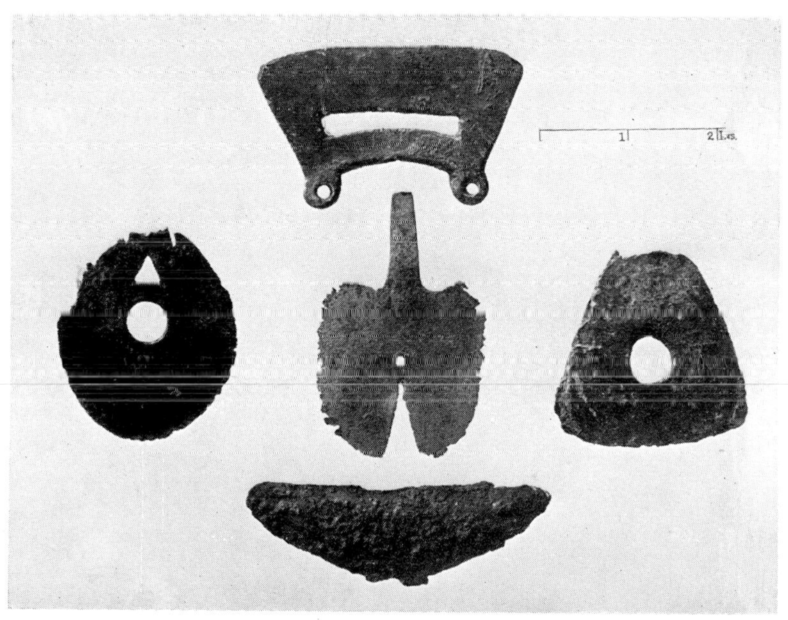

PLATE XIV [*By permission of the British Museum*

Bronze razors of various types. (See page 20.)

PLATE XV [*By permission of the British Museum*

Early English bronze tools and weapons. (See page 24.)

CHAPTER III

Copper in the British Isles

Copper in Pre-Roman Times.

The spread of the great Roman Empire carried with it an increasing knowledge of metallurgy, and in due course many refinements in the art of metal working were brought by the Romans *via* Spain to this country.

Although the Roman occupation undoubtedly led to a considerable increase in the production and use of copper and bronze in the British Isles, the use of these metals was already well established before the arrival of the invaders. Crude copper implements which may date as far back as 2500 B.C. have been found in Ireland, while bronze objects possibly as old as 1800 B.C. have been found in both England and Ireland. The workmanship displayed in most of these early relics, however, is not very good.

It is possible that the early Aryan inhabitants of Central Europe were acquainted with copper, and it is not unlikely that it was some of their more adventurous brethren who first introduced its use into this country.

The earliest English bronze objects have been found in the round burial barrows of the Late Neolithic period, and the fact that only small objects have been found in conjunction with more plentiful pottery remains, suggests that the bronze age was only just beginning at that time.

Some of the earliest metal working was probably introduced by the Brachycephalic or short-headed invaders from Europe, who mixed with the Dolichocephalic, or long-headed inhabitants of the country, to form the mixed population which appears to have existed here during the round barrow period.

Bronze implements have been found much more frequently in the earliest burial mounds in the south than in the north, and it is thought, therefore, that the southern tribes were better or earlier provided with bronze than the northern. This is as might be expected if metal working was first introduced from the Continent and gradually spread over the interior to the north of the island.

The occurrence of tin and copper ores in close proximity in Cornwall certainly provided favourable conditions for experiments in metallurgy, but it is unlikely that any metal was worked in this country before about 2000 B.C., at a time when bronze had been known to the Egyptians for at least a thousand years.

It is interesting to note that Strabo (54 B.C.—24 A.D.) records that the Phœnicians carried on a trade in tin from Cadiz, a port which may have been founded by them not later than about 1100 B.C., partly for the purpose of carrying on trade with Cornwall, which was nearer than Tyre or Sidon.[1] It is believed that the Phœnicians were acquainted with the mineral deposits in Britain as early as 1500 B.C., and it is probable that copper or bronze was already in use by the inhabitants at that time.

At first these metals were used only for small objects, such as the pins and buttons found in the earliest barrows, but as the art of metal working progressed so the range of uses for copper and bronze was gradually extended. Objects such as plain axe-heads or celts, knife daggers, drills and awls have been found in later burial mounds, while swords, spearheads and various types of daggers and celts as well as gouges and chisels are characteristic of a still later period. The weapons and implements illustrated in Plate XV were found in the founder's hoard at Bexley Heath in Kent, and are representative of those in use during the latter part of the Bronze Age in this country. At the bottom of the illustration will be noticed two small round cakes of copper such as would be produced by metal run into the shallow circular cavity at the bottom of the earliest type of smelting furnace described in Chapter I.

The large cauldron and bucket shown in Plate XVI are typical examples of rivetted bronze vessels which have been found in various parts of this country and in Ireland. The

[1] STRABO. "The Geography of Strabo," vol. 1, p. 262.

cauldron on the left was recovered from the River Thames near Battersea, while the bucket was found at Dowris in Kings County, Ireland. They date possibly from about 700 B.C. and are now in the British Museum.

Copper in Roman Britain.

According to Strabo, in spite of the care which the Phœnicians took to keep secret the purpose of their voyages from Cadiz, the Romans eventually found their way by sea to Cornwall. There is also evidence that as early as about 600 B.C., overland trade routes also existed via Bordeaux and the valleys of the Loire and the Rhone to Marseilles. Many changes in the population of these islands had taken place, however, before the arrival of the first Roman colonists in 55 B.C. The Picts had been driven northwards by Celtic pioneers from the Continent, who in due course were themselves driven westward by the Brythons and, although the production and working of metals had by that time been established, they were not in a very well developed state.

The Romans mined copper extensively in several parts of the country, notably in Cumberland, North Wales and Anglesey, but there is little evidence that they worked any mines in Cornwall or Devon. Roman cakes of copper found in North Wales are to be seen in the British Museum. It is probable that much of the metal was exported, and it is interesting to note that one cake found near an old mine at Llandudno was stamped with the words "Socio Roma"—"to my partner at Rome".[1]

During the period of the Roman occupation the arts of metallurgy appear to have thrived, but upon their departure at the beginning of the 5th century much of the progress ceased and throughout the dark ages which followed comparatively little headway was made. For several centuries very little copper was produced, and it was not until the latter part of the 16th century that a new beginning was made with the mining and smelting of copper in this country. By this time considerable metallurgical progress had been made abroad, and practically all the copper as well as most of the manufactured metal goods

[1] GOWLAND. "Copper and Its Alloys in Early Times." *J. Inst. Met.*, vol. 7, (1912), p. 40.

used in this country were imported. The economic development of England lagged very much behind that of the Continental countries, where the Germans were particularly famous for their skill in metal working and their industrial enterprise.

Bell-Founding.

One of the few metal industries which had made some early headway in this country was that of bell-founding. There is evidence that bells were cast in China from bronze many centuries B.C. Roman bells were cast from Campanian brass—hence the name "campanile" for a bell tower—which Pliny regarded as the most suitable metal. After the time of Constantine, clappers or bells were commonly used by Christians to summon people to their assemblies. Bells of a considerable size were used in convents in England as early as the sixth century, likewise in Gaul, and even earlier in Ireland.

One of the earliest records of bell-founding in England is an entry amongst the tenants of Battle Abbey late in the 11th century A.D., when a reference is made to "Aedric who cast bells". It is also recorded that four bells for the Chapel of Windsor Castle were made in 1250 from material left over from the casting of the great bell of Westminster, while the quaint bell-maker's window in York Minster, which depicts two bell-makers at work, is thought to date from about 1200.[1]

From that time onwards bell making appears to have been a prosperous industry in this country. There were numerous foundries, particularly in London and East Anglia, which became famous for their work, and the experience which they obtained in the casting of bronze for bells proved to be of great value also for the manufacture of cannon when they were introduced at a later date. The mediæval English name for a bell-founder was "bellyeter", and it is from this word that Billiter Street in London derived its name, since it was a former centre of the industry in that area.

The Production of Ordnance.

It is believed that cannon were used by the English for the first time during the reign of Edward III, either at the siege of Cambrai in 1339 or at Crecy in 1346, and it is possible that guns of copper were made in this country a year or two later.

[1] SALZMAN. "English Industries in the Middle Ages" (1923), pp. 145-146.

PLATE XVI

Bronze cauldron and bucket; c. 700 B.C. (See page 24.)

PLATE XVII

[*Photographed by permission of the Resident Governor of the Tower of London*

Turkish breech loading gun, A.D. 1464. Weight, 18 tons. (See page 27.)

Such weapons were employed by the Germans in Italy, at the siege of Cividale in 1331. Probably the first recorded instance of brass guns being made in this country was in 1385, when three brass cannon are said to have been made by the Sheriff of Cumberland.

Most of the early guns were breech loaders and were made in two parts, the barrel being attached after loading to the chamber which contained the charge. Later, however, they were cast in one piece and finished by boring. At first the guns were small but as their size increased the amount of copper, bronze and brass used in their construction became very considerable, particularly in the case of the heavier types of cannon, such for instance as those used by the Turks in early times.

An interesting large breech loading gun made from bronze, now to be seen in the Tower of London, is shown on Plate XVII, and it will be noted that it was made in two parts which were screwed together after loading. According to an inscription, the gun illustrated was made in 1464 for Sultan Muhammad Khan. It was one of forty-two similar guns mounted on the shores of the Dardanelles, twenty-two on the North side and twenty on the South. Each gun weighed about 18 tons, had a calibre of 25 in. and fired stone shot weighing about 6 cwt. Although over 300 years old at the time, they were used with great effect in 1807 against an attacking British squadron and caused considerable losses, for it is recorded that one shot alone killed and wounded sixty men.

The Revival of the Copper and Brass Industry in the 16th Century.

Although London appears to have been an important centre for the manufacture of ordnance and the foundries were by no means idle, at the beginning of the reign of Henry VIII, large numbers of guns were being imported from abroad, in addition to most of the copper required for the home production of ordnance. The dependence on foreign supplies of copper for this purpose caused some uneasiness, however, and prompted Henry VIII to encourage the mining in this country of both copper and calamine, the latter being needed for the production of brass. Men skilled in the art of mining and smelting were brought over from the Continent.

In the year 1565, during the early part of Elizabeth's reign, copper was once again being produced in Cumberland from a mine which had been started near Keswick. English gun making made rapid strides and by the end of the century cannon were actually being exported.

Copper and brass were also used extensively in the form of wire for wool cards. The woollen industry being one of the most important in the country, required large numbers of these cards, for whereas the long woollen fibres used for the production of worsteds were combed, the short fibres had to be carded, a process which worked the wool into a fluffy mass of inseparable fibres prior to spinning. Hand cards were wooden instruments with a handle, on one side of which were wire teeth set in leather. Wool was placed between two of them and they were then worked in every direction to produce a mass of interlaced fibres. Although carding machinery was invented by Paul in 1748 it did not come into general use until it had been improved by Lees and Arkwright some years later.[1]

Up to the time of Elizabeth the drawing of copper or brass wire was a very primitive process in this country. Only man power was available, and one method was for two men seated on swings facing one another to have a narrow strip of brass between them fastened to a belt around each of their waists. By propelling the swings with their feet they were able to swing apart and gradually produce a crude type of wire by stretching the brass.[2] Wire was also produced by hammering until that method was superseded by the process of "drawing", which is believed to have been used for the first time at Nuremberg in the 14th century. At first the wire was pulled through the die by hand, but later machinery driven by water or other motive power was used.

Brass wires for wool cards were mostly imported until towards the end of the 16th century when wire-drawing machines worked by water power were introduced from abroad in Elizabeth's reign, and a wire-drawing industry was started in this country.

[1] HEATON. "Yorkshire Woollen and Worsted Industries." (1912), p. 333.
[2] HAMILTON. "English Copper and Brass Industries to 1800." (1926), p. 344.

The First Copper and Brass Producing Companies.

In 1566, a rich copper deposit was discovered at Newlands near Keswick and ore mined there was smelted in works established at Brigham. In the same year a search was made for calamine and deposits were discovered at Worle in Somerset. Two years later in 1568, the first great copper producing company, which had been in operation since 1564, was incorporated, and became known as the Mines Royal. In the same year another company, the Mineral and Battery Works, founded in 1565, also received a charter of incorporation. The latter company was granted very wide powers, with exclusive rights to mine calamine and make brass and engage in the process of battery and wire drawing; battery being the process whereby sheets of metal were produced by hammering. The company had established works at Tintern Abbey, whence the calamine from the Somerset mines was taken to be made into brass, some portion of which was drawn into wire; but at first production was only experimental, and it was not until 1568 that brass was satisfactorily produced.

It is of interest to note that the Mines Royal and the Mineral and Battery Works were the first joint stock companies in England whose business was exclusively home manufacture. In this connection it may be mentioned that the first joint enterprise of any kind was a company formed to work a copper mine at Falun in Sweden. The mine was in operation in the 13th century and is still worked and owned by the same company. which is now the oldest in the world.

In 1582, an attempt was made to start up the long neglected copper mines in Cornwall, and smelting works were set up at Neath in South Wales. Difficulty was experienced with water in the mines, however, and they had to be abandoned after a year or two. At the time copper and brass were used extensively, not only for such purposes as guns and wire but also for the manufacture of many other articles, such as pots and kettles and similar utensils which were beaten into shape from sheet metal. Wool cards were made in the London and Bristol areas and a brass factory was started at Isleworth in 1582, to meet the requirements of the industry.

The manufacture of brass pins had by this time become an industry of considerable importance, and at the accession of James I it was stated that no less than 20,000 people were engaged in the trade, though the figures may be open to some doubt since they were put forward by the pin makers as part of their argument when endeavouring to persuade the Government to grant them protection from foreign competition.[1] It is of interest to note that in 1543 it was considered necessary to prohibit by law the sale of pins unless they were "double-headed and have the heads soldered fast to the shank".[2] This particular law, however, was soon repealed.

At the time of the Civil War copper mines were being worked in North Wales and Anglesey as well as in Cumberland; and although those in North Wales and Anglesey, being outside the sphere of operations, fortunately escaped damage, both the mines and works in Cumberland were completely destroyed.

[1] HAMILTON. "English Copper and Brass Industries to 1800." (1926), p. 47.
[2] 34 & 35, Henry VIII, c. 6.

DRAWING COPPER WIRE BY WATER POWER, 16TH CENTURY.

PLATE XVIII

[*Reproduced with the permission of the Director of the Victoria and Albert Museum*

Indian copper figure of Shiva. 8th or 9th Century.
Cast by the cire perdue process.

PLATE XIX.

[*Reproduced from "The English Brass and Copper Industries to 1800"*

A battery works. (See page 32.)
From Duhamel du Monceau: Description de la Manufacture du Cuivre: établie près d'Essone: 1764.

CHAPTER IV

The Development of Industry

An Extension of Mining Facilities.

In the second half of the 17th century, it became evident that the monopoly for copper mining held by the Mines Royal was having a very bad effect upon the development of the industry, which reached such a degree of stagnation in 1689 that the Mines Royal Act was passed. This Act destroyed the monopoly and gave anyone the right to mine copper. The way was thus left open for private enterprise, and fresh deposits of copper were soon discovered, and many new enterprises started. The industry developed, and the battery works supplied large quantities of copper and brass sheets and wires, not only to the factories but also to domestic workers and craftsmen who turned them into a large variety of implements, household utensils and ornaments.

Although bronze had been cast for many years in the making of bells and cannon, it was not until towards the end of the 17th century that the art of brass casting began to be applied to general uses. In 1693 John Lofting, a London merchant, was granted a patent for the manufacture of thimbles,[1] which up to that time had been mostly imported from Holland. The patent related to certain "engines" used for their production in conjunction with a method of casting, and he set up works at Islington to exploit the process.

The thimbles were cast in special sand obtained at Highgate and were finished by means of the special "engines". It is recorded that six gross of thimbles were made at one cast, and that the factory, which employed three men and three boys, produced on an average 140 gross of thimbles per week.[2] It was not long, however, before a vast brass founding industry had developed from such small beginnings as these, and the

[1] British Patent (1693), No. 319.
[2] Houghton. "A Collection of Letters for the Improvement of Husbandry and Trade." (1697), vol. 2, No. 260, p. 194.

rapidity with which the trade in copper and brass ware increased can be judged by the fact that between 1710 and 1720 the export trade alone increased by nearly nine times.

Manufacturing Processes.

Battery has already been referred to as a process whereby sheet metal was produced by hammering. Hammers worked by water power were introduced into this country from Germany upon the formation of the Mineral and Battery Works in 1565, and the process was in general use until it began to be superseded by rolling in the 18th century. The copper or brass for battery was cast into moulds and the ingots so produced were annealed in a coal and charcoal fire before being beaten into plates of required thickness by means of a large variety of hammers, some weighing as much as 500 pounds.

For the production of articles the plates were cut up into smaller pieces of suitable shape, usually circular, by means of shears, the larger sizes of both shears and hammers being worked by water power. Several pieces of plate were then placed together, one on top of the other and the hammering continued, the articles being finally worked into shape by the hammering into a sort of mould, a process which is illustrated in Plate XIX, which shows the interior of a battery shop in 1764. It will be noticed that in the centre of the illustration plates are being cut with shears, while at each side the discs of metal are being hammered into shape by means of different types of power-driven hammers.

Very many battery works existed in various parts of the country and the process was used exclusively until power-driven rolls were introduced late in the 17th century. At the beginning of the 18th century, a large rolling mill was erected at Maidenhead on the Thames, while another one was in operation at the Mitcham copper works, where copper sheets were produced for coinage. Although the process of rolling gradually superseded that of battery for the production of metal strip and sheet, articles made from sheet copper and brass continued to be made by the battery process until late in the 18th century, when mechanical presses began to be used.

The Production of Wire.

Brass for the production of wire was usually made in small pots containing about 10 or 12 pounds of metal each, the contents of 8 or 10 such pots being mixed together and cast into flat plates between large blocks of stone. These plates, which weighed about 70 pounds each, were cut into seven or eight strips and passed through the rolling mill, being annealed occasionally as required. The strips having been rolled to appropriate size, were cut up again into threads, which were then drawn through successively smaller holes in iron plates.[1]

In 1649, a battery and wire works had been established at Esher in Surrey, using copper imported from Sweden, but by 1697 these works had been taken over by William Dockwra and some others and used only home produced copper. It is stated that these were the only works in the country at the time that had 24 wire drawing benches installed; these were worked by water power and about a ton of wire was produced each week. Most of it was used for pin making, and after drawing it had to be cleaned so that no scale or dirt remained on the surface. This was accomplished by a process known to-day as "pickling", but whereas the material to be cleaned is now immersed in an acid solution at the wire works, in those days the wire in coils was taken to the starch-makers or distillers and was placed in their waste acid liquors. It was afterwards scoured and rubbed with the pulp of rotten oranges to give it a smooth clean finish, and after re-drawing was usually made into pins by hand. It is recorded that some of the best workers were able to produce as many as 24,000 pins per day.[2]

A novel process for casting copper into plates was that employed for many years in Japan, into which country the art of metal working was introduced probably from China. The Japanese became particularly skilled in the work and many of their production methods were as ingenious as they were unique.

Although in Japan bronze was extensively cast into ornamental forms, the casting of copper was confined to plates, rods and discs, which were then hammered into whatever shape was required. The metal was cast in shallow canvas trays submerged

[1] HOUGHTON. "A Collection of Letters for the Improvement of Husbandry and Trade." (1697), vol. 2, No. 258.
[2] *Ibid.* No. 259, pp. 192-3.

in a bath of hot water. The molten copper was poured through the water into the tray and immediately the metal had solidified the red hot plate was lifted out and held for a moment in the steam rising from the hot water. It was then thrown back at once into the bottom of the tank. The momentary exposure of the casting to the steam produced a permanent and beautiful deep rose-coloured layer of oxide on the surface of the metal, which gave it a very attractive appearance. Up to 1873 all Japanese copper was cast by this process, though it has since been superseded by more up-to-date methods.[1]

The large Japanese bronze Buddha shown in Plate XX was cast about the end of the 16th century and serves to illustrate the high degree of skill in the production of ornamental bronzes which had been attained by that time in Japan.

Technical Developments.

In this country considerable technical advances were made during the 18th century. In 1738 William Champion took out the first patent for making zinc from calamine ore.[2] The metal had been known for many years, having been found in smelting furnaces and elsewhere, but no method of producing it intentionally was known in Europe until this time, although it had been produced probably many years previously in India and China, where slabs of zinc 98 per cent. pure dated 1585 A.D. have been found in the Kuangtung Province.

In 1742, Thomas Bolsover of Sheffield showed how silver could be plated over copper. The discovery was made accidentally, for while preparing a knife in which both copper and silver were used, he perceived that by a process of beating and rolling the two metals could be made to unite, so that a silver surface could be obtained on a copper foundation.[3] This was merely a rediscovery, however, since copper articles "plated" with silver were used both by the ancient Greeks and by the Egyptians. Although Bolsover's idea was not adopted until some time later and was used at first only for the plating of small articles such as snuff-boxes and buttons, it proved to be the beginning of a large

[1] GOWLAND. "Art of Metal Working in Japan." *J. Inst. Met.*, vol. 4, (1910), p. 29.
[2] British Patent (1738), No. 564.
[3] GATTY. "Sheffield—Past and Present." (1873), p. 137.

trade in silver plated copper articles and it was not long before Sheffield plate, on account of its excellent quality, was in big demand. The process continued in use until the introduction of the electroplating process which gradually superseded it.

In 1769, John Pickering, a London gilt toy-maker, patented a machine for impressing designs on sheet copper and brass by means of hammering sheet metal on to a raised die or model,[1] and a few months later, Richard Ford, a Birmingham man, improved on the invention by using a raised die and corresponding sunken mould into which it fitted.[2] The new process was particularly suited to the production of saucepans, kettles, buttons and similar articles, and made mass production possible, probably for the first time. So effective was it in speeding up production that it is recorded that towards the end of the 'Eighties in that century, Matthew Boulton was able to produce over 30,000 copper coins per hour by means of the presses installed in his works at Soho in Birmingham.

The commercial production of zinc, following upon the discoveries of William Champion, enabled James Emerson to start experimenting with the making of brass from copper and zinc instead of calamine, and in 1779, he set up a works at Henham to manufacture brass by the new process, which he patented in 1781.[3] Metallic zinc did not, however, at once supersede calamine for brass making, and the ore was still being used in England even as late as the middle of the 19th century. At about the same time as this new process was started, rolls driven by water power were introduced to replace the old process of battery, but it was not until the steam engine had been perfected by Watt that the older process was finally discontinued.

Steam Power and the Copper Industry.

When Watt went to Birmingham in 1774, he had already achieved some success with his steam engine, and, as a result of his partnership with Boulton, it was not long before the new engines were on the market. They were at first applied almost exclusively to pumping and soon found a ready market

[1] British Patents (1769), No. 920.
[2] *Ibid.* (1769), No. 935.
[3] *Ibid.* (1781), No. 1297.

in the Cornish copper and tin mines, where considerable difficulties had always been experienced with water.

Pumping engines made by Newcomen were already in use at the mines when the first Boulton and Watt engine was erected in 1777, and its introduction gave rise to some hostility from those in the locality who were prejudiced in favour of the older type. However, the first two engines erected at Wheal Busy near Chacewater and at Tintang near Redruth very quickly demonstrated their superiority from the point of view of both power and economy, and numerous others were ordered, with the result that in 1780, of 40 pumping engines which had by then been produced by Boulton and Watt, 20 were working in the mines of Devon and Cornwall.[1]

The pumps were patented, and the users were required to pay premiums to the makers, the premiums being based upon the savings which the pumps effected; thus Boulton and Watt became intimately connected with the copper mining industry, and very much concerned with its prosperity. Although the pumping engines did much to increase the productivity of the Cornish mines, and were responsible for prolonging the life of many of them, these mines had great difficulty in competing with the Anglesey producers, and much bitter rivalry ensued.

In 1787, the Cornish mines produced 4,768 tons of copper, and those in Anglesey 4,000 tons, while at the same time large quantities were also imported, mainly from Spain. The competition led to drastic price cutting, and the price of copper fell to low levels, but whereas during these years the mining industry in this country experienced difficult times, the manufacturers became exceedingly prosperous.

Copper Smelting in South Wales.

In 1583 works were set up under the auspices of the Mines Royal at Neath in South Wales to smelt the copper ore obtained from the mines in Cornwall, and it was from this early enterprise that South Wales later developed into the copper smelting centre of the world, a position which it held until about the middle of the 19th century.

Before the smelting operations at Neath started, copper had

[1] Samuel Smiles. "Lives of Boulton and Watt." (1865), pp. 230, 231, 262.

been smelted at Keswick, but progress in the development of the art had been slow and about 22 weeks were required to produce copper from the ore. Technical developments in the South Wales area, however, progressed so rapidly that copper was soon being produced from the ore in less than 5 days, with the result that the Cornish mines were unable to deliver the ore as quickly as it was required, and thus copper began to be sent to South Wales from all parts, the careful mixing of the different kinds of ores so received greatly facilitating the process of smelting.

The plant at Neath was extended in 1695, and about 1717 the first smelting works were set up at Swansea. In the early days at Keswick wood and charcoal were used for smelting, but in 1632 Edward Jorden discovered a new method of smelting by using pit coal, peat and turf as a fuel,[1] and four years later Sir Phillibert Vernatt was granted a patent for the use of coal alone as fuel for metal working.[2] These inventions and others which followed them did much to promote the copper smelting industry in the Neath and Swansea districts, where abundant supplies of coal were available which could be obtained at a low price, particularly as the best coal was not required, and that which was unsuited to other purposes could be used. Swansea was also an excellent seaport and was accessible to ships from all parts of the world which could bring ore from mines abroad, and thus it was that the smelting works of South Wales continued to prosper late in the 19th century in spite of the fact that copper mining in Great Britain had begun to decline by about 1840.

At the end of the 18th century Great Britain was the largest producer of copper in the world, and supplied about 75 per cent. of all the copper produced, much of it from Cornish ores, while practically the whole of the world's supply was extracted by the Swansea smelters.[3] In 1830, the large copper deposits in Chile began to be developed, followed at intervals

[1] Brit. Patents (1632), No. 61.
[2] *Ibid.* (1636), No. 91.
[3] LEVY. "Modern Copper Smelting." (1912), p. 5.

of a few years by those of Australia, North America and Spain, each new development adding to the already continuous procession of ships converging upon Swansea from all parts of the world, bringing copper ore to be smelted and taking coal in return.

The technique of modern copper production owes much to the early work done in South Wales, where a good deal of the plant was developed which is now used so extensively in the smelting and refining of copper, such, for instance, as the reverberatory furnace, which was in use in Swansea as early as 1698.

As the vast copper deposits abroad were developed, so the production of Cornish ores decreased, and in time the ore produced in distant parts, instead of being sent to Swansea for smelting, was smelted where possible at works set up in the vicinity of the mines. Expert smelters from this country travelled to all parts of the world to teach others how to carry out the work, with the inevitable result that within a comparatively short time Swansea could no longer boast of being the centre of the world's copper production.

Increasing Production.

In the latter part of the 18th century the ever-increasing demand for small articles such as buckles, buttons, toys and brass foundry goods was augmented by the entirely new market for heavier goods, the demand for which had been greatly increased by the introduction of steam power, and the revolutionary industrial developments which followed.

Brass cylinders were required for pumps and engines, together with a vast range of fittings, such as grease caps, gauge covers, whistles and other accessories. It also became necessary to produce alloys suitable for the manufacture of steam valves and cocks, and many different types of brasses and bronzes were invented to withstand the combined effects of heat and steam pressure. An increasing amount of attention was also being paid to sanitation and water supply, and the requirements of the plumbing trade, together with those of the carriage and furniture trades at a time when the prevailing fashion called for elaborate brass ornamentation, resulted in a great increase in the consumption of copper and brass.

As the number of the different kinds of articles increased it became impossible for individual craftsmen to possess all the tools and patterns which were required for their production; this resulted in the trades becoming very much specialised and thus it was that by the end of the 18th century there existed a large number of special trades, such as the compass makers, hinge makers, cock makers, hat-pin makers, and many others.

Not only did the home market for the copper and brass industry increase very rapidly during this time, but a considerable export trade was also built up. In 1731, the East India Company started to export large quantities of copper in cake form to the East, and in 1751 the trade was extended to include manufactured copper in sheet or other form, with the result that between 1774 and 1791 nearly 27,000 tons of copper were exported. The extent to which the export trade to other parts had also been developed is shown by the fact that just prior to the war with France in 1792, about one-quarter of the articles produced in Birmingham were exported to France and Italy.

THE 'ROCKET', 1829: COPPER FIREBOX PLATES AND TUBES; BRASS STEAM FITTINGS.

CHAPTER V

Copper in the Electrical Industry

The Birth of the Electrical Industry.

At the beginning of the 19th century there came that ever increasing interest in electrical matters which within a few years laid the foundations of the wonderful age of electricity as we know it to-day. The rapid progress of electrical engineering has been due in no small measure to the existence of copper. It has played a vital part in every phase of electrical development, and without it our vast present-day electrical industry would in all probability not have existed.

Copper was intimately connected even with the discovery of some of the very earliest electrical effects, such, for instance, as that made by Galvani in 1786, when he noticed the curious behaviour of some frogs' legs hung by means of a copper hook from an iron railing. The experiments of Galvani excited much interest and encouraged others to investigate the new phenomena, with the result that in 1799 Volta made the first electric battery, known as "Volta's Pile", which he described for the first time in 1800. This, like many other batteries which followed, employed copper as an active element, for it consisted of discs of copper and zinc placed one upon the other with a layer of wet cloth between each pair. The use of wet cloth as a separator may be accounted a lucky chance, for although it was believed that the electricity arose from the contact of the metals, the part played by an electrolyte in the action of a cell was not appreciated at the time.

Some idea of the rapid development of the primary battery following the appearance of "Volta's Pile" may be gained from the fact that only a few years later, in 1809, John Children constructed a battery having 20 pairs of plates of copper and zinc, each plate being 6 feet long and 2 feet 8 inches wide. No less than 320 square feet of copper sheet were required for the battery, the cells of which had a total capacity of 945 gallons.[1] It was with the aid of this battery that Children conducted experiments to determine the best conductor of electricity and was thus probably one of the first to give scientific proof of the superiority of copper for this purpose.

Another large battery in use at about the same time was that installed at the Royal Institution with which Davy and Faraday performed many of their experiments. This had 2,000 pairs of plates of copper and zinc with a total surface of no less than 890 square feet.

Lightning Conductors.

Copper was also used for lightning conductors for the protection of buildings, and in 1811 it was employed in a similar capacity for the protection of ships' masts. Prior to this time it was customary for ships to carry copper chains which were hoisted to the tops of the masts whenever there appeared to be any danger from lightning. Contact with the water was made by means of a connection outside the hull. As might be expected, the hoisting of the chains was not always carried out with sufficient speed, with the result that the ship was often damaged before they could be got into position. It was thought advisable therefore, that the conductors should remain permanently in position and at the suggestion of Benjamin Cook copper strips were run down each of the masts and through the hull to the ship's bottom, which was often sheathed with copper as a protection against fouling. The fact that the conductors were not always an unqualified success was not in any way a reflection upon the quality of the material employed, but rather upon the method of its installation, as will be evident when it is noted that in one Man-of-War at least a conductor actually passed through the powder magazine.[2]

The Introduction of the Telegraph.

One of the first useful applications of electricity was for the purpose of signalling, and very many systems of telegraphy were invented and tried out before Cooke and Wheatstone in 1837 installed on a section of the London and North-Western

[1] MOTTELAY. "Bibliographical History of Electricity and Magnetism" (1922).
[2] STURGEON. "Lectures on Electricity." (1841), p. 207.

Railway between Euston and Chalk Farm the first electric telegraph to be put into commercial use. In 1843, a similar installation was put into service between Paddington Station and Slough. These sytems employed copper conductors and required five wires which were supported in grooved wood blocks. In 1846, the first commercial telegraph company was formed, and by 1866, three such companies owned between them no less than 16,000 miles of line.

No sooner had the telegraph been established successfully on land than attempts were made to adapt it for submarine working, and in 1850, Jacob and Watkins Brett laid a single copper wire covered with gutta percha between England and France. The cable, which was unarmoured, broke unfortunately after only one day's operation. It was replaced, however, a year later with an armoured cable having four separately insulated solid copper conductors, which proved to be entirely satisfactory.

Several successful submarine cables were laid in the next year or two before the first attempt was made in 1857 to lay a cable across the Atlantic. The magnitude of this undertaking may be judged from the fact that no less than 17,500 miles of No. 22 gauge copper wire had to be drawn to make the 2,500 miles of conductor which were required.[1] Although the first attempt failed, a second attempt with 3,000 miles of cable was successful. The cable, however, failed after only a few weeks' working, and it was not until yet another unsuccessful attempt had been made in 1865 that a completely satisfactory cable was laid and put into commercial operation in 1866. Over 365 tons of copper were required for the manufacture of the conductor of this cable. It is interesting to note that the contract for this cable involved the first production of "High Conductivity" copper. Owing to the great distance involved, the time-lag in the original signals made them blurred on arrival at the receiving end. Lord Kelvin (or Sir William Thomson, as he was at that date) traced the fault to the copper not being quite pure, and insisted upon a purer metal; this resulted in the production of the now familiar "H.C." grade.

[1] Bright. "Life of Sir Charles Tilston Bright." Vol. 1 (1899), p. 130.

PLATE XX

[*Reproduced with the permission of the Director of the Victoria and Albert Museum*

Japanese cast bronze Buddha. 16th Century.
(See page 34.)

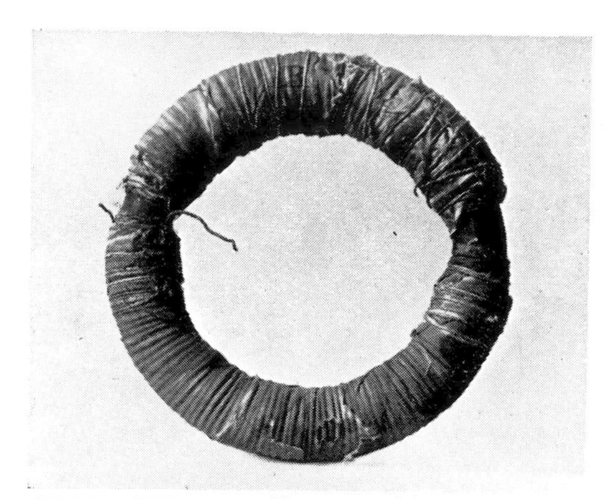

PLATE XXI [*By courtesy of the Royal Institution*

Faraday's electro-magnetic induction ring.
Diameter, 6 ins. (See page 44.)

PLATE XXII [*By courtesy of the Hackbridge Electric Construction Co. Ltd.*

A modern electrical transformer.
Capacity, 93,750 K.V.A. Weight, 96 tons. (See page 44.)

The Development of Electrical Machines.

Although the electric battery sufficed for the supply of current for telegraphic purposes, the need for a more abundant source of supply was appreciated and considerable attention given to the development of electrical machines. The electro-magnetic investigations of such men as Oersted, Ampère, Sturgeon and Arago paved the way for the greatest of all discoveries, those of Faraday in 1831. It was in that year that he discovered the effects described by him as "Volta-electric" and "Magneto-electric induction", one or other of which is the underlying principle of almost every electrical apparatus or machine since constructed.

The first magneto-electric machine made by Faraday in 1831 consisted of a copper disc 12 inches in diameter, which was revolved by hand between the poles of a permanent magnet, and from that time the design of electrical machines developed rapidly, with the result that within a few years power driven generators were in commercial use. In 1841, multipolar machines were being used in Birmingham for the electro-plating of copper articles, and in 1858, a generator for an electric light was installed in the North Foreland lighthouse.

It is interesting to note the extent to which the size and output of generators increased, for, whereas the armature of Faraday's machine required only about 7¼ lbs. of copper, the armatures of a machine built by Wilde, details of which were given in a paper before the Royal Society in 1866, required 576 lbs. of copper strip and wire.[1] This belt-driven machine was described at the time as "a machine of enormous and unprecedented power", for its output "was so enormous as to melt 15 inches of No. 11 copper wire". As a comparison it may be noted that the rotor of a modern turbo-generator such as the 105,000 kw. machine installed in the Battersea Power Station of the London Electric Power Company, although operating at several hundred times the voltage of Wilde's machine, requires about 11 tons of copper, nearly 24 tons being required for the whole machine, which is many thousand times more powerful than that described by Wilde in 1866.

[1] Proceedings of the Royal Society. Vol. 15, April 26, 1866, p. 107.

While the action of all electrical generators of this type is based upon Faraday's discovery of "magneto-electric induction" the action of all electrical transformers and similar apparatus is based on his discovery of "electro-magnetic induction". Plate No. XXI shows a photograph of the apparatus used by Faraday in his first successful experiment in this connection. The apparatus, which is now one of the treasured possessions of the Royal Institution, is in fact the first electrical transformer ever constructed. It consisted of a soft iron ring 6 inches in diameter upon which were wound five lengths of copper wire. Three lengths of wire were wound on one side of the ring and two on the other. About 130 feet of copper wire were used in all, the turns being insulated from one another with twine and calico.[1]

Some idea of the remarkable developments which followed this epoch-making discovery of Faraday may be gained by referring to a transformer of modern design such as is illustrated in Plate XXII. This unit, which is representative of present-day practice, is one of two installed at the power station at Barking near London. They are some of the largest transformers in the world, each having a capacity of no less than 93,750 K.V.A. The photograph shows the inside of the transformer before being placed in its containing tank, which is filled with oil. Each complete unit weighs 165 tons and about 20 tons of copper in the form of 43 miles of conductor strip and wire were required for its manufacture.

The size and design of this type of apparatus have been developed to such an extent that the modern production no longer bears any resemblance to Faraday's experimental ring, but it is interesting to note that although it has been possible to make very great improvements in nearly all of the other materials used in its construction, the latest product still employs conductors of copper substantially the same as those used by Faraday over one hundred years ago.

The Transmission and Distribution of Electricity.

Coincident with the development of generation, numerous systems for the distribution of the current were devised. All of these used copper conductors either in the form of rod or

[1] JONES. "Life of Faraday." (1870), vol. 2, p. 2.

wire, which material has been used almost exclusively for the purpose ever since. To-day, many miles of copper wire may be required for the distribution of electricity within a single building, and many thousands of tons of the metal are in continuous service in the form of both underground and overhead distribution cables in all parts of the world.

As the demand for electricity developed, schemes for the transmission of power over greater distances were devised. Voltages increased, and in 1890 the first high voltage underground mains in this country were installed by Ferranti between Deptford and London. Four mains, each about seven miles long, were laid and put into service at 10,000 volts. The conductors in each main consisted of two concentric copper tubes insulated with resin-impregnated paper, the diameter of the inner tube being about 0·8 ins. and that of the outer 1·9 ins.; they were made in 20 ft. lengths, and nearly 140 tons of copper were required in all.[1]

A year later, in 1891, the first demonstration of long distance three-phase high-voltage transmission by means of an overhead line took place in Germany at the Frankfort-on-Main Electrical Exhibition. This installation, which was the forerunner of our present extensive high voltage transmission systems, employed three copper wires supported on porcelain insulators and wooden poles. The line was 110 miles in length, and was used to transmit power derived from generators at Lauffen on the Neckar to Frankfort, where it was used to light the exhibition and work the exhibits.

In spite of the fact that the conductors were only 4 mm. in diameter, nearly 60 tons of copper were required for their manufacture. The line was run at about 20,000 volts, and, although it remained in service for only a short time, it effectively demonstrated the possibilities of long-distance transmission and the suitability of the materials employed.

A modern development of this early transmission experiment is the National Grid System erected in this country, of which the line shown in course of erection in Plate XXIII is a part. The towers illustrated are those carrying the conductors which

[1] *The Electrician*, Sept. 4, 1891.

cross the River Thames at Dagenham below the London Docks. The river at this point is one of the busiest waterways in the world, and it was essential when designing the crossing to ensure that all materials used were absolutely the most reliable obtainable. The length of the span between the supporting towers is 3,060 ft., and in order that ample clearance should be given under all conditions for the masts of ships passing on the river, it was necessary that the conductors at the lowest point of their sag should never be less than 250 ft. above the high-water level, with the result that the supporting towers, at present the largest of their type in the world, had to be no less than 487 ft. in height, or more than two and a half times as high as Nelson's Column in Trafalgar Square in London.

At this height over exposed country it is to be expected that the pressure exerted by the wind on the conductors, together with the additional weight of accumulated ice or snow which they may have to carry, render the conditions very onerous, and in this instance these conditions were made even more exacting by the corrosive nature of the polluted atmosphere in the district. Under the circumstances, therefore, in view of the fact that the highest possible degree of reliability was essential, an all-copper-alloy cable was adopted. Each of the seven cables, which are made up from 91 phosphor bronze and cadmium copper wires and are nearly 1 in. in diameter, could support a weight of more than 25 tons, and as no joints were allowed in the cables each had to be manufactured in one continuous length of about 6,400 ft., weighing over 6 tons.

It is perhaps of interest to note in connection with this modern development that stranded bronze wire cables were made even in ancient times. Among the several examples which have been found one piece of cable fifteen feet long, found in Pompeii, which was in use there before the destruction of the city in A.D. 79, consisted of three cables, each composed of fifteen bronze wires, twisted round each other.[1]

[1] NEUBURGER. "The Technical Arts and Sciences of the Ancients." (1930), p. 37.

PLATE XXIII

[*By courtesy of the Central Electricity Board and the main contractors, Callender's Cable & Construction Co. Ltd.*

A high voltage electrical transmission line crossing the river Thames at Dagenham. Height of towers, 487 ft. Span, 3,060 ft. (See page 45.)

PLATE XXIV

The bronze gates of Henry VII's Chapel, Westminster Abbey. Early 16th century.

(See page 52.)

CHAPTER VI

Architectural Uses of Copper

Copper and bronze have always had a high intrinsic value which is independent of the form in which they may exist, and in every age it has been the custom in times of need to raid the architectural storehouse and commandeer the metal for more urgent purposes, such as the replenishment of depleted coffers or the manufacture of armaments. Thus it is that much of the old architectural copper and bronze is no longer in existence to-day in the form in which it was originally used.

Copper in Sumerian Construction.

The Sumerians (4000—3000 B.C.) were one of the greatest nations of pioneer craftsmen the world has ever known and were probably the first to employ many of the fundamental structural principles, such as those of the arch and the dome, for the introduction of which credit has in some cases been given to others. The earliest known examples of mosaic work are of Sumerian origin, and there is evidence that their skill in metal working was of a high standard.

The excavations which have been carried out in Mesopotamia show that the Sumerians made extensive use of copper, gold and silver. The two latter materials were used mainly for decorative purposes, sometimes in conjunction with copper or bronze, which metals were nearly always employed when any useful purpose had to be served. Thus, for instance, copper nails and pins sometimes had gold or silver heads so that they might be both useful and decorative at the same time. Several examples of purely decorative copper work have been discovered, however, such as the large relief depicting a lion-headed eagle holding two stags which was found at Al'Ubaid and referred to on page 19. Among the smaller objects which have been found are a number of small copper figurines, possibly representing goddesses. These figures, which had probably a religious significance, are peg-shaped and would appear to have been driven into the unbaked bricks or other parts of the structure to act as protectors of the building. Similar figures of a later type were used to support stone tablets bearing inscriptions.[1]

There is evidence to show that copper played an important part in Sumerian wooden structures, and although the wood of many of the objects which have been found had almost disappeared the copper parts and fittings remained to give a clue to their original form and purpose. The Royal Graves at Ur were found to abound in such objects, although in some instances the unusual form of the remaining metal parts has rendered it difficult even to guess at either the nature or the purpose of the original structures.

The earliest known references to wheeled vehicles tend to indicate that this form of transport may have been introduced first by the Sumerians. It is worthy of note therefore that copper was used in conjunction with wood for the construction of wagons as well as for other forms of structure. In "The King's" Grave at Ur, in addition to the copper helmets, spears and other equipment of what appears to have been the king's bodyguard, were found also the remains of a woodwork wagon, and although the wood was considerably deteriorated the copper bolts, which had been used to secure the body of the wagon to the axle shaft, remained.[2]

Egyptian Copper Work.

The Egyptians were a people extremely skilled in the arts of architecture and building, and their early ornamental metal work and skill in casting were of a particularly high standard. They were pioneers in the production of hollow castings and used copper extensively for both architectural and decorative purposes. The metal in sheet form was often beaten into shape and nailed to a wooden framework for support or was used for the capping of stone obelisks and the sheathing of other structures.

[1] Rolfe. "The Story of Early Metallurgy." *Metal Ind., Lond.*, Oct. 12, 1928, p. 341.

[2] Woolley. "Ur Excavations—The Royal Cemetery." (1933), vol. 2, pp. 63-4.

As has already been mentioned, wrought copper sheets were used to make water pipes. The sheets were rolled into short tubes which were then joined together by inserting their ends one into the other. The completed pipe, after being laid in a rock trench and covered with gypsum, proved to be so durable that sections over 4,000 years old are in existence to-day. Gates and doors, together with their supporting pillars, were often made of copper, and in this connection the paintings found at Thebes in the tomb of Rekh-mi-Rē, who lived about 1471 to 1449 B.C., are of interest, for they depict the casting of copper doors for the great temple at Karnak.

The Mycenæan copper nails found at Orchomenus, and other similar objects, show that copper continued to be used for structural purposes in the early Mediterranean civilisations, a fact which would appear to be confirmed by the descriptions of metallic architectural wonders to be found in Greek literature, some of which are believed to refer to the glories of the earlier Cretan and Mycenæan civilisations. Nevertheless, it was not until about the time of the Roman Emperors that any considerable extension of the use of copper and its alloys took place.

In addition to the use of copper and bronze for such things as nails and cramps, the covering of walls and doors, and for decorative parts in buildings the metals were also used in conjunction with appliances for the supply water. Roman water pumps were frequently made of copper or bronze, as were the stop cocks, valves and other fittings, although the pipes were generally made of lead. Presumably as a result of this practice the dangers of lead poisoning had already made themselves apparent even at that time, for Vitruvius, an expert in such matters, refers to the subject in his treatise *De Architectura*, which he wrote at a date probably not later than 27 B.C. After pointing out the danger to health he remarks, "Therefore it seems that water should not be brought in lead pipes if we desire to have it wholesome".[1]

[1] VITRUVIUS. "De Architectura." Trans.: Granger. Vol 2, Book 8, c. vi, p. 189, paras. 10 and 11.

Copper Roofs.

In Roman times copper was also used as a roofing material. The dome of the Pantheon at Rome, one of the largest in the world, was formerly roofed with bronze tiles. It is recorded that after they had been removed by Constans II and carried off to Constantinople in A.D. 663 they were captured *en route* by the Saracens. The original cornice round the central opening or drum of the dome, however, is still in existence, and it is not unlikely that the tiles also exist in some form or another to-day. Under the tiles was a sheathing of copper plates. This was removed by Pope Urban VIII nearly one thousand years later, in 1632; it yielded him 200 tons of copper sheet, in addition to 4 tons of copper nails.

It is worthy of note that the great dome of the British Museum, the diameter of which is only two feet less than that of the Pantheon, is roofed with copper, although in this case it has only been in position since 1857; and there are many other notable examples of copper roofs, among which might be mentioned that of the Chapel Royal of St. James's Palace, the dome of the Old Bailey, London, two domes on the recently built Bank of England (besides large quantities of copper gutters, down pipes and rain-water heads), the roof of Guildford Cathedral and the roof of the new Liverpool Cathedral; the last-named building, which is still unfinished, contains more than thirty tons of copper sheets.

In addition to the great durability and pleasing appearance of copper which results from the formation of a green patina with prolonged exposure to the atmosphere, the metal has many other advantages as a roofing material. It will not "creep" on steep slopes and since it can be laid in very thin sheets the reduction in the weight of the roof may be very considerable. It has been estimated, for example, that if the dome of St. Paul's Cathedral had been covered with copper sheet (as was proposed by Parliament) instead of lead, the weight of the roof would have been reduced by many tons. Such a reduction in the weight to be supported would undoubtedly have rendered the maintenance of the stability of the fabric of Wren's masterpiece a less harassing task than it has been.

Considerable quantities of copper have been used in the past for such purposes as gutters and flashings, particularly during the 18th century and onwards, not merely in Western countries but also in the Far East, for in Japan the metal was also used extensively in architecture for roofing, gutters, spouts and many ornamental features. Copper is very largely used on roofs in Sweden and Denmark; at Copenhagen the Vesterport Building, which is 320 feet long and 160 feet wide, is entirely sheathed in copper, of course with copper gutters and down pipes. At the present time the world wide use of copper for such purposes is rapidly increasing, for in addition to its superiority from a technical point of view its use results in an important saving, not only in first cost but also in maintenance charges.*

Copper and Bronze Doors.

Since the days of the Romans one of the principal architectural uses of bronze has been for ornamental doors and gates. Unfortunately, many of the earliest examples are no longer in existence, and it is believed that not more than sixty-four sets of bronze doors older than the 16th century remain to-day. The bronze doors of the Pantheon, which were erected by the Emperor Hadrian when the building was restored about 124 A.D., are said to be the only ones now remaining *in situ*, though it is probable that others which have been transplanted may still be in existence.

Early Greek doors dating from about the 6th century are to be seen at St. Sophia, in Constantinople, and in St. Mark's, Venice. The former doors were ordered by Justinian in 543 and were made of wood four or five inches thick overlaid with bronze plates. About three centuries later the first Frankish doors were cast for Peterhausen and the Cathedral of Aix-la-Chapelle.

There are a few examples of German bronze doors dating from about the 11th century, but by far the most numerous are those of Italian origin, from the 12th to the 15th century. Among the many beautiful examples which remain may be mentioned the doors of the Florence Baptistry which are particularly notable for their exquisite workmanship, parts of which

*Full technical information on this subject is included in C.D.A. Publications Nos. 42 and 25, "Copper Flashings and Weatherings" and "Copper Pipe-Line Services in Building" respectively.

were executed by Lorenzo Ghiberti. It is recorded that 20 artists were occupied for 21 years in finishing the first set of these doors.

Although bronze was usually employed for doors and gates, there are one or two notable examples of copper doors still existing to-day, such as the beautiful Moorish doors to the Court of Oranges in the Mosque of Cordoba in Spain, which are made of copper plates on wood.

Few examples of early bronze doors or gates exist in England, and probably the oldest are the gates of Henry VII's Chapel in Westminster Abbey. These gates, which are amongst the most treasured possessions of the Abbey and are illustrated in Plate XXIV, were the work of Torrigiano and date from the beginning of the 16th century. More recently, bronze has been used in this country to an increasing extent for ornamental doors of all types, and a typical example is illustrated in Plate XXV.

Grilles, Weather-vanes and Finials.

Copper and bronze have also been used in the past, to a lesser extent, for such architectural purposes as railings and grilles. One early example of a protective grille made of pierced copper sheet, which dates possibly from the fifth or sixth century, is to be found in the Church of the Nativity at Bethlehem, while a particularly beautiful example of a somewhat later bronze grille dating from the 15th century can be seen in the Chapel of the Sacred Girdle in the Cathedral of Prato. To-day bronze is used very extensively for such purposes and many beautiful examples are to be seen.

Among other architectural uses of copper and bronze one of the oldest is for weather vanes and finials. It is recorded that when Andronicus of Syria built the Tower of the Winds at Athens in the 1st century B.C., he placed on the top of it a bronze Triton holding a rod in his hand which was so constructed that it was revolved by the wind, and thus indicated its direction.[1] Since that time innumerable similar devices have been erected, and of the many to be seen in this country, some made of pierced copper sheet date probably from as early as the 14th century, while more modern examples are to be seen almost everywhere.

[1] VITRUVIUS. "De Architectura." Trans.: Granger. Vol. 1, Book 1, c. vi, p. 57, para. 4

Lightning Conductors.

Copper is also used extensively for the protection of buildings from damage by lightning. In biblical days the immunity of Solomon's Temple from such damage was attributed to Divine Providence, rather than to the metal with which the building was covered. A different state of affairs seems to have existed in England at a later date, however, for Fuller records that even the ringing of the bells, which, according to superstition, was supposed to ward off lightning, proved quite ineffectual, and that "there was scarce a great abbey in England that was not burnt down with lightning from Heaven."[1]

A work entitled "L'Instruction", written in 1560 by Philibert de l'Orme, an architect of the Tuileries, shows that architects at that period also had to contend with thunderstorms, but it was not until two centuries later that Franklin, as a result of his experiments, was responsible for the erection of the first lightning conductors on buildings in this country. In 1769, Franklin's lightning conductors were erected on St. Paul's Cathedral. These conductors were made of iron and it is recorded that notwithstanding the fact that they were 4 in. by ½ in. in section, their electrical resistance was so high that when the cathedral was struck by lightning in 1772 portions of a conductor were made red hot by the passage of the discharge. Since those days much attention has been given to the subject and considerable quantities of copper are now used in lightning conductor systems for the protection of buildings.

Copper Tubes.

With the present-day tendency to concentrate on the qualities of materials as governing design, with a consequent increase of interest in research work, it is not surprising that copper is coming into general use for a great number of other building and architectural purposes, and one of its most important applications is for tubes.

For many years, on account of its exceptional resistance to corrosion and fouling, it has been necessary to employ copper for water pipes in the interests of health wherever the nature of the water is such that it may react to a serious and sometimes dangerous extent with other metals. Now that the other

[1] FULLER. "The Church History of Britain." (1655). Edited : Brewer. Vol. 3, Book 6, p. 342, para. 3.

advantages of copper pipes for water systems are being realised, however, their use is rapidly extending. The employment of thin-walled tubes, the introduction of simpler jointing methods, and the present-day moderate price of copper, are factors which have combined to render generally available those advances in the technique of plumbing which have hitherto often been considered as luxuries only for the few. The corrosion-resisting properties of copper tube, its smooth bore and the ease with which it can be installed are advantages which make it particularly suitable for use also in connection with drainage systems.

Another purpose for which copper tubes are now being used to an increasing extent is for the conduits which contain the wires of an electrical installation in a building. For this purpose copper has many advantages over other materials, for not only is it cheap to install, but it is not subject to rusting or other deterioration, and thus provides a very safe and lasting installation. It is for these reasons that many of the finest contemporary buildings, such as that of the Bank of England in London, are fitted throughout with copper tubing.

Copper and its alloys have long been used extensively for interior decoration, for which purpose their warm and pleasing appearance renders them particularly suitable. Large quantities of these metals are used to-day, not only for purely decorative work but also for such purposes as metal furniture and lighting fittings, and it is worthy of note that modern finishing methods are capable of preserving the desirable appearance of the metal without any necessity for frequent cleaning.

Copper is also an admirable material for use as a metal facing and as copper-faced plywood or in other sheet form it is found to provide a ready solution to many sheathing and structural problems; while among the many other uses for copper, bronze and other copper alloys in architecture may be mentioned masonry cramps, wall ties and damp-courses, window-frames, shop window and similar fittings, balustrades and railings. This latter application is illustrated in Plate XXVI which shows the bronze railings, lamp standards, lighting fittings and other bronze metalwork used in present-day bridge construction.

PLATE XXV.

A modern bronze door.
(See page 52.)

PLATE XXVI.

Bronze railings, lamp standards and other metal parts in bridge construction. (See page 54.)

PLATE XXVII

A bronze propeller for the Cunard liner "Queen Mary". Weight, 35 tons.
(See page 56.)

CHAPTER VII

Copper To-day

The great increase in the production of copper during recent decades is itself a striking testimony to the ever-increasing demands for the metal from all quarters.

For example, in 1944 the world production of copper was nearly 3 million tons, whereas during the first ten years of this century the world production averaged only about 600,000 tons per annum. In 1939, the consumption of copper in the United Kingdom was almost 260,000 tons. During the war, the incessant demand for copper and its alloys for a thousand types of war materials resulted in a great increase of consumption, attaining in the peak year a figure not far short of 500,000 tons in Great Britain alone. This great demand for war purposes necessitated a serious curtailment during the war years of copper supplies for normal purposes, but with the return of peace the 1939 figure for consumption has been far exceeded, the British consumption during 1951 being 555,858 tons, of which about 330,000 tons was virgin copper.

In normal times, more than one-half of all the copper produced is used in the electrical industry and approximately one-fifth in shipbuilding, the remainder being employed for a vast range of purposes of every kind.

In the electrical industry, copper is used mainly in the form of strip, bars, wires or tubes for conductor purposes. The wires are of every description, from a simple length of bare conductor to a highly elaborate cable comprising many strands of copper in a number of concentric layers. Their uses are as varied, including cables and wires for the distribution of electricity, the electrical wiring of buildings for heat, light and power, trolley wires for all types of electrical traction, and wires for all forms of commercial and domestic electrical apparatus and machinery.

There is also an ever-increasing use of copper for communication purposes, for telephone and telegraph wires, cables and instruments, and for radio and television equipment, all of which would not be possible without copper.

One of the greatest developments of the war was in connection with radiolocation and communications generally. The vital part played by copper in these developments can be judged by the fact that in 1943 5,800 tons of copper were consumed per month in the production of the United States Army Signal Corps equipment alone.

In the shipbuilding industry, copper and its alloys are used extensively in ships' engines and their condensers and also for propellers, shafts, bearings, and general fittings of every kind, since it is very necessary that such parts shall not deteriorate or become corroded when exposed to the salt-laden atmosphere prevailing at sea. Plate XXVII shows one of the propellers of the giant Cunard liner "Queen Mary". The ship is fitted with four such propellers, which are made of manganese bronze. They are 20 feet in diameter and weigh about 35 tons each.

Another important use of copper is for the treatment of ships' bottoms. It was first applied as a sheathing for British warships in the 32-gun frigate "Alarm" in 1761, and by 1783 almost every ship in the British navy had a copper bottom. Modern sheathing applied to the bottom of vessels is often made of "Muntz's metal", an alloy of copper and zinc, but the largest use of copper for the treatment of ships' bottoms is in the form of anti-fouling paint.

Copper is of great importance in the transport industry for components of road and railway vehicles. In the manufacture of motor cars, in addition to the copper used in such vital parts as the ignition, starting and lighting systems, it is also required for radiators, oil, petrol and hydraulic brake pipes, brake linings, bearings, gaskets and numerous brass pressings and hot stampings. In the case of the railways, not only is a considerable amount required for electrification purposes, but it is used also in steam locomotives and other rolling stock for such purposes as boiler tubes and plates, fireboxes and stays, steam and oil pipes, valves, bearings and brake mechanisms, as well as in the brass fittings of passenger coaches.

The locomotive illustrated in Plate XXVIII is one of the modern British Railways Standard Class 7, 4-6-2 Mixed Traffic locomotives, with a boiler pressure of 250 lb./sq. in. and a tractive effort of 32,150 lb. The copper firebox, which has an overall length of approximately 10 feet, is 7 feet 1 inch wide and 7 feet 0½ inch high and is made entirely of copper ⅝ inch thick except for the tube plate, which is 1 inch thick.

It is interesting to note that the first fire tube boiler ever constructed was that which provided the steam for the pumping engine at Wheal Busy in Cornwall, to which reference has already been made in Chapter IV. At the suggestion of Boulton in 1780 this boiler, which was 26 feet in length, was fitted with four copper tubes each 20 inches in diameter; the flames from the fire passed through two of them and returned by the other two.[1] In spite of this early example, however, the fire tube boiler appears to have been practically reinvented some years later for application to steam locomotives, in which it is used at the present time, in a slightly modified form.

Copper as a metal is also used extensively for many purposes in the dairy, brewing, chemical, laundry and other industries, while in the form of one or other of its salts it plays an important part in the manufacture of such things as colours and pigments, medical preparations, insecticides and water purifiers. Plate XXIX illustrates the use of copper for large vessels such as are often required in the above-mentioned industries. The tank shown, which is for the purpose of storing acid, has a capacity of 46,850 gallons and was made entirely from copper sheets welded together into three main sections.

Copper for fungicides has been used for many years in the spraying of potatoes and vines. The mixture used is a copper sulphate solution, with lime (Bordeaux mixture) or soda (Burgundy mixture) added, according to the purpose. A solution of copper is also widely employed for the rot-proofing of timber and fabrics.

[1] SAMUEL SMILES. "Lives of Boulton and Watt." (1865), p. 283.

Small quantities of copper are often added to cast-iron and steel for the purpose of improving the metal and rendering it more resistant to corrosion. Many thousands of tons of such copper-bearing material are in service to-day.

A very large quantity of copper (usually in the form of brass) is used for such small articles as pins, boot eyelets, buttons, hooks and eyes, fasteners, hinges, door and window fittings, and a host of other everyday objects.

The Virtues of Copper.

In many cases, particularly in the Electrical Industry, metal of the highest possible conductivity is required, and for such purposes copper having a purity of at least 99·95 per cent., can be produced without difficulty. The fact that metal as pure as this can be obtained from ore which often contains less than two per cent. of copper is a high tribute to the skill and ingenuity that have been exercised in the development of modern production methods.

The exceptional ductility and toughness of copper, which are of importance particularly from the manufacturing point of view, are effectively demonstrated by the ease with which it can be rolled into flat sheets less than one five-hundredth of an inch in thickness, or drawn into wire having a uniform thickness of only one thousandth of an inch; a single pound of copper being sufficient for the production of over sixty miles of such wire.

Although copper in the annealed state is soft and easy to work, when necessary its strength and hardness can be increased very easily by cold working, that is to say by hammering, rolling or drawing the metal when cold. By this means alone the hardness and tensile strength of copper can be more than doubled. When a still stronger or harder metal is required the properties of copper can be adjusted to suit almost any purpose by the addition of small proportions of other metals. This, however, is a subject of great complexity, for there are literally hundreds of alloys in commercial use, in which copper is the predominant element. For example, if it is desired that the electrical conductivity of the alloy shall not be lowered to any great extent, a small proportion of cadmium may be added The addition of less than one per cent. of this metal considerably

PLATE XXVIII

[*By courtesy of British Railways*

The "William Shakespeare", a 4-6-2 Mixed Traffic locomotive.

(See page 57.)

PLATE XXIX. *By courtesy of the Aluminium Plant and Vessel Co. Ltd.*

A large welded copper acid storage tank. 46,850 gallons capacity.
(See page 57.)

increases the tensile strength of copper but does not seriously affect its conductivity.

Stronger alloys still can be produced by the addition of small quantities of other metals. For instance, the addition of 5 per cent. of tin is sufficient to double the strength of copper, while the inclusion of a small percentage of beryllium makes it as hard and strong as high grade steel. Alloys of this latter type are also notable for their exceptional resistance to fatigue with rapidly varying load stresses, and are, therefore, particularly suitable for the manufacture of springs and for other purposes in which this very valuable property is required.

As might be expected in view of its very high electrical conductivity, copper is also an excellent conductor of heat; it is for instance about six times as efficient as iron in this respect. Its high thermal conductivity, which is greater than that of any metal except silver, makes it an ideal material, therefore, for use for all purposes where heat has to be transferred, such as in the case of heating or cooling apparatus, cooking vessels, water heaters, radiators, milk coolers, refrigerators and similar devices.

Unlike many other metals, copper is not only easy to fabricate but it can be jointed without any difficulty by soldering, brazing or welding. This feature is of the greatest importance, not only in the jointing of electrical conductors but also in the joining of copper water pipes, and similar operations, as well as in the manufacture of the multitude of articles now made from copper.

The freedom from deterioration and the extraordinary lasting qualities of copper cannot be demonstrated better than by the very fact that copper objects thousands of years old are in existence to-day. These objects, to some of which reference has been made in the foregoing pages, have withstood the severe combined effects of both atmospheric and subterranean conditions since the dawn of civilisation, and of all man-made things can most truly be said to have withstood the tests of time.

Sources of Supply.

In ancient times the Eastern Mediterranean deposits formed the source of copper supply for the early civilisations which existed in that neighbourhood, and although the sources from which the Sumerians derived their copper are not known with any certainty it is possible that they may have obtained supplies from the Arghana deposits between Kharput and Diarbekr, which are now worked by the Turkish Government, while another source of supply is believed to have been located in the State of Oman in Arabia.

The Egyptians obtained much of their copper from the mines in the Sinai Peninsula, which were worked long before 3200 B.C. Inscriptions in the tomb of Thutmose III in Egypt, which date from about 1500 B.C., show that copper was sent to Egypt from Cyprus as a tribute in the form of elegantly designed vases and vessels of beautiful workmanship, a fact which tends to indicate that at that time copper working had been long established in the island. Research work has shown that the copper deposits in Cyprus were worked probably as far back as 3000 B.C., while more than two millenia later in Greek and Roman times they still formed the source of a great portion of the copper supplies.

It was from the name of this island that our word "copper" was derived, for the Romans referred to copper as "Cyprian metal" or "aes cyprium". The word "aes" was eventually omitted and "cyprium" became corrupted to "cuprum", from which our word "copper", the German word "Kupfer", and the French word "cuivre" were derived.

The Romans also obtained copper from the deposits at Rio Tinto in Spain, from which large quantities of metal are still being produced to-day. In North America most of the copper was originally obtained from the native deposits of the Lake Superior region, and in the East copper mines were worked in the Honan Province of China probably as early as 2500 B.C.

The deposits in this country from which, towards the end of the eighteenth century, the major portion of the world's copper supply was obtained, are now no longer worked, and our requirements are met by supplies imported from the more prolific deposits abroad. It is pleasing to note, therefore, that a large proportion of these deposits lie within the British Empire.

The major portion of the world's present copper supply is

PLATE XXX

[*By permission of the British Museum*

Large copper relief from near Ur (about 3100 B.C.). (See page 19.)

obtained from deposits found in Canada and other parts of North and South America, Northern Rhodesia and Central Africa, Spain, Australia and Japan. The Canadian and Northern Rhodesian deposits, which are among the richest in the world, are alone large enough to supply the Commonwealth's requirements for many years to come and it is their recent rapid development that has been largely responsible for the complete change in the copper position which has taken place within a very short space of time.

In 1931, only 17 per cent. of the copper imported into Great Britain was of Empire origin, but in the following year the proportion was increased to 40 per cent., while in 1950 77 per cent. of the imported copper was produced within the Empire and it is possible that the proportion will continue to increase. If necessary, Empire production is undoubtedly sufficient to meet all our requirements.

The Economic Aspect.

The development of these new sources of supply and the introduction of more efficient production methods resulted in a very material reduction in the price of copper, and the price before the war was almost as low as at any time for at least 150 years. One penny would buy about ten times its own weight of copper, which can, therefore, no longer be considered as a semi-precious metal; it is for instance much less expensive than stainless steel and considerably cheaper to fabricate. Although since the war prices of almost all raw materials have risen steeply, it is expected that in the future copper will remain relatively cheap and plentiful, and that there will be a considerable development of its many uses.

Notwithstanding the fact that the first cost of copper is not at present low, the money involved in its purchase is really only invested, for not only does copper give long and trouble-free service, but unlike most other materials, it is always worth a considerable proportion of its original cost in scrap value. Any depreciation is usually only a very moderate charge for years of efficient service.

BIBLIOGRAPHY

AGRICOLA, GEORGIUS —De Re Metallica (1556).
Trans.: H. C. and L. H. Hoover (1912).

BAIN, H. FOSTER and WM. G. SCHNEIDER—Copper (1933).

BRIGHT, CHARLES —The Life of Sir Charles Tilston Bright (1899).

BURY, J. B. —The Cambridge Ancient History, Vol. 1 (1924).
Edited: J. B. Bury, S. A. Cook, F. E. Adcock.

COFFEY, GEORGE —The Bronze Age in Ireland (1913).

COLLINS, W. F. —The Corrosion of Early Chinese Bronzes.
J. Inst. Metals: Vol. 45, No. 1 (1931), p. 23.

DAVIS, WATSON —The Story of Copper (1925).

DESCH, C. H. —Sumerian Copper.
Reports of Brit. Assoc. for Advan. of Science, 1928 to 1933.

ELAM, C. F. —Some Bronze Specimens from the Royal Graves at Ur.
J. Inst. Metals: Vol. 48 (1932), p. 97.

FLEMING, J. A. —Fifty Years of Electricity (1921)

FULLER, THOMAS —The Church History of Britain (1655).
Edited: J. S. BREWER, 1845, Vol. 3.

GARLAND, H. and BANNISTER, C. O. —Ancient Egyptian Metallurgy (1927).

GATTY, ALFRED —Sheffield—Past and Present (1873).

GEERINGS, G. K. —Metal Crafts in Architecture (1929).

GOWLAND, WILLIAM —The Metals in Antiquity.
J. Royal Anthropological Institute: Vol. 42 (1912). p. 235.
—Copper and Its Alloys in Early Times.
J. Inst.Metals: Vol. 7, No. 1 (1912), p. 23.
—The Art of Working Metals in Japan.
J. Inst.Metals: Vol. 4: No. 2 (1910), p. 4.

HAMILTON, HENRY	—The English Brass and Copper Industry to 1800 (1926)
HEATON, H.	—Yorkshire Woollen and Worsted Industries (1920).
HOLMES, T. RICE	—Ancient Britain and the Invasions of Julius Cæsar (1907).
HOUGHTON, JOHN	—A Collection of Letters for the Improvement of Husbandry and Trade. Vol. 2 (1697), Nos. 257-8-9, 260-1.
JONES, H. B.	—The Life of Faraday (1870).
LEEDS, E. THURLOW	—A Bronze Cauldron from River Cherwill with Notes on Other Bronze Vessels. *Archæologia*, Vol. 80 (1930).
LEVY, D. M.	—Modern Copper Smelting (1912).
MUNRO, ROBERT	—Prehistoric Britain (1912).
MONTELIUS, OSCAR	—The Chronology of the British Bronze Age. *Archæology*, Vol. 11 (1909), p. 97.
MOTTELAY, PAUL F.	—A Bibliographical History of Electricity and Magnetism (1922).
NEUBURGER, ALBERT	—The Technical Arts and Sciences of the Ancients. Trans.: H. L. Brose (1930).
PHILLIPS, G. B.	—Primitive Copper Industry in America. *J. Inst. Metals:* Vol. 34, No. 2 (1925), p. 261; Vol. 36, No. 2 (1926), p. 99.
RICKARD, T. A.	—Man and Metals (1932). —The Early Use of Metals. *J. Inst. Metals:* Vol. 43, No. 1 (1930), p. 297.
ROLFE, R. T.	—The Story of Early Metallurgy. *The Metal Industry:* Oct. 12, 1928, p. 341.
SALZMAN, L. F.	—English Industries of the Middle Ages (1923).
SMILES, SAMUEL	—Lives of Boulton and Watt (1865).
STRABO	—The Geography of Strabo. Trans.: H. C. Hamilton and W. Falconer, Vol. 1 (1854).
STURGEON, WILLIAM	—Lectures in Electricity (1841).
THOMPSON, SILVANUS	—Dynamo-Electric Machinery (1904) —Light—Visible and Invisible (1897).
VITRUVIUS	—De Architectura. Trans.: F. Granger, Vols. 1 and 2.
WOOLLEY, C. L.	—Ur Excavations—The Royal Cemetery (1933).
YETTS, W. PERCIVAL	—The Catalogue of The Eumorfopoulos Collection.

A Guide to Antiquities of the Bronze Age —British Museum (1920).

Copper in Architecture —The Copper and Brass Extended Uses Council (1927).

The Electrician April 24, 1863; Sept. 4, 1891.

The Proceedings of the Royal Society—Vol. 15, April 26 (1866), p. 107.

British Patents —No. 61 (1632).
—No. 91 (1636).
—No. 319 (1693).
—No. 564 (1738).
—No. 920 (1769).
—No. 935 (1769).
—No. 1297 (1781).

Making Brass in 1781

No attempt has been made in the foregoing pages to include technical or other information of a practical nature.

Such information is given in special publications issued by the C.D.A., a list of which will be found on the next page, and these, together with other information relating to the use of copper and its alloys, can be obtained, free of charge by those giving evidence of responsible status or genuine interest, from

THE COPPER DEVELOPMENT ASSOCIATION

KENDALS HALL, RADLETT, HERTS.

Telephone: Radlett 5616

LIST OF AVAILABLE C.D.A. PUBLICATIONS

(See note on page 65.)

---

3. *Copper Through the Ages* (Historical and general).
6. *Brasses* (Engineering and metallurgical data).
12. *Copper Data* (Engineering and metallurgical data).
15. *Bearing Bronzes* (Engineering and metallurgical data).
16. *Brass, Bronze and other Copper Alloy Wire and Wire Products* (Engineering and metallurgical data).
21. *Copper as a Mould Material* (Reprinted from the *Metal Industry*).
22. *Copper for Bus-Bars* (Technical data for electrical engineers).
23. *Copper in Chemical Plant* (Copper as a material of construction).
25. *Copper Pipe-Line Services in Building* (Practical handbook for architects, builders and plumbers).
26. *Copper and Brass Pressings* (Engineering and metallurgical data).
29. *Copper in Cast Steel and Iron* (Technical data for foundrymen, metallurgists and engineers).
30. *Copper for Earthing* (Technical data for electrical engineers).
31. *Aluminium Bronze* (Technical data for metallurgists and engineers).
34. *The Machining of Copper and Its Alloys* (Technical data for engineers).
36. *Classification of Copper and Copper Alloys* (Reprinted from *Metallurgia*).
37. *Mechanical Loading Tables for Overhead Lines* (Technical data for electrical engineers).
38. *Copper Alloy Resistance Materials* (Technical data for electrical engineers).
39. *Copper and Copper Alloy Springs* (Technical data for engineers).
40. *Copper Underground: its Resistance to Soil Corrosion* (Technical data for engineers).
41. *Copper Compounds in Agriculture and Industrial Microbiology* (mainly on fungicides and insecticides, for farmers, etc.).
42. *Copper Flashings and Weatherings* (Practical handbook for architects, builders and plumbers).
43. *Copper and its Alloys in Engineering and Technology* (Technical data).
44. *Equilibrium Diagrams of Binary Copper Alloys* (Technical data for metallurgists).
45. *Copper Conductors for Overhead Lines* (Reprinted from the *I.E.E. Journal*).
46. *Copper: its Ores, Mining and Extraction* (Semi-technical, for schools, etc.).
47. *The Welding, Brazing and Soldering of Copper and its Alloys* (Technical data for engineers).